OXFORD LATIN COURSE I WORKBOOK

TEACHER'S EDITION

Maurice Balme & James Morwood

OXFORD UNIVERSITY PRESS 1992

Oxford University Press, Walton Street, Oxford OX2 6DP

Oxford New York Toronto
Delhi Bombay Calcutta Madras Karachi
Petaling Jaya Singapore Hong Kong Tokyo
Nairobi Dar es Salaam Cape Town
Melbourne Auckland
and associated companies in
Berlin Ibadan

Oxford is a trade mark of Oxford University Press

First published 1992

Workbook ISBN 0 19 912165 6
Teacher's Edition ISBN 0 19 912166 4

Acknowledgements
The authors and publishers would like to thank John Ditchfield, Julian Morgan, Jonathan Powell, Roger Rees and Gaby Wright
Illustrations by Cathy Balme
The publishers would like to thank R. L. Dalladay for permission to reproduce the photograph on page 34 and the Rev. E. Buckley for keying in the text
All other photographs were taken by James Morwood

Printed in Hong Kong

INTRODUCTION

The Pupils' Workbook contains a variety of exercises intended to consolidate and develop the material of the coursebook. It should be used flexibly; teachers will not want, and will not have time, to work straight through the book but should select some exercises for oral work and others for written homework.

The first sets of exercises in each chapter aim at sharpening pupils' understanding of grammar. We are aware that the coursebook itself does not provide enough practice in grammar for any but the ablest pupils and that continual revision is necessary; the variety of approach offered by these exercises may make the task more palatable and it should be possible to do them very quickly.

All chapters contain an exercise aimed at developing pupils' awareness of the relationship between the English and Latin languages. These are valuable in widening pupils' vocabulary in both English and Latin and enhancing their perception of how different languages work.

We attach great importance to the exercises that are intended to encourage pupils to use Latin actively and to sound it expressively and correctly; we believe that they will lead to a quicker, more intelligent and more accurate reading of Latin. These exercises are of three sorts:

Cartoons are attached to most chapters accompanied by the rubric: 'Describe in Latin what is happening in this picture'. These are best treated orally and can produce a lively and stimulating interlude. If time does not allow this, pupils may be asked to provide written answers for homework; in the latter case the length and sophistication of the answers will differ according to the pupils' ability. We provide specimens of the sort of answers pupils might be able to give on p. 63 below.

Every fifth chapter there is a playlet instead of a cartoon. These are intended to provide an opportunity for pupils to speak Latin expressively and correctly. See *Oxford Latin Course: Teacher's Book*, p. 9 for advice on pronunciation.) We are well aware that shortage of time continually restricts efforts to make pupils sound the Latin language and can only say that the more pupils speak and sound the language aloud, the quicker and more reliable their progress will be.

3 Short dialogues to be read aloud in pairs. These begin at chapter 6. Teachers should make sure that the Latin is understood before the readings begin.

If activity **1** – with the cartoons – proves successful, teachers may choose to photocopy the cartoons from the beginning of some of the chapters in the coursebook, tippex out the captions, and make a transparency to be shown on an overhead projector and discussed in Latin with the class. Some suggestions for questions on the cartoons in the first two chapters of the coursebook are given in this Teacher's Edition.

In every chapter there are questions or activities that build on the paralinguistic elements of the course. These are pitched at varying levels of sophistication, and teachers will wish to drop a number of them as being inappropriate to their pupils. Most chapters end with a *bonne bouche* which we hope may provide some diversion late on a Friday afternoon!

A final activity, not included in this book, is recommended to render sentence analysis more digestible. Teachers can write out some of the exercises from the coursebook on a transparency and, using an overhead projector, invite the participation of the whole form and write in s, v, o, etc. above the appropriate words, acting on the form's suggestions.

In this Teacher's Edition we fill in the answers to most of the questions in the pupils' book. We do not, of course, give answers to the open-ended questions. As well as possible answers on the cartoons in this book, we give some sample questions on the early cartoons in the coursebook (p.64). In addition we include four attainment exercises, to be tackled after chapters 6, 10, 15 and 20, with their answers.

Maurice Balme
James Morwood

CONTENTS

CHAPTER I

(a) *Complete the following sentences by giving the correct Latin form for the words in brackets; then translate. For example:*

Scintilla cēnam parat (is preparing). — Scintilla is preparing dinner.

1 Scintilla Horatiam (Horātia) vocat. — Scintilla calls Horatia.

2 Horātia Scintillam (Scintilla) salūtat. — Horatia greets Scintilla

3 puella (The* girl) Scintillam iuvat. — The girl helps Scintilla.

4 puer culīnam intrat (enters) sed nōn labōrat.
The boy enters the kitchen but does not work.

5 Scintilla in culīnā laborat (is working). — Scintilla is working in the kitchen.

6 Scintilla filiam (her** daughter) vocat. — Scintilla calls her daughter.

7 fīlia culinam (the kitchen) intrat et Scintillam iuvat (helps).
The daughter enters the kitchen and helps Scintilla.

8 puer Scintillam salutat (greets) sed Horatiam (Horātia) nōn iuvat.
The boy greets Scintilla but does not help Horatia.

* omit 'the' ** omit 'her'

(b) *The following words are derived from Latin. Fill in the blanks so that the sentence makes sense:*

irate **culinary** **response** **horticulture**

Tom ran in from the garden and gave Julia a kiss. She made no response since she was busy cooking. Tom smelt the saucepan and said, 'Oh no! I don't think much of your culinary efforts.' She was very irate and snapped back, 'Well, at least it's more productive than your attempts at horticulture.'

(c) *Describe in Latin what is happening in this picture:*

(d)

1 How did people become slaves?

2 What was the difference between a slave and a freedman?

3 How could slaves become free?

4 Look at the picture of the Roman nobleman on page 11 of the coursebook. Why do you think he is carrying the heads of his forefathers carved in stone? See if you can find out what the robe he is wearing is called.

5 Identify as many as you can of the tools of the trade of the two freedmen in the picture on page 12 in the coursebook. Next lesson ask your teacher what is on the left of the stone. What do you think this stone was used for?

(e)

Across

1 Quīntus in Apūliā ________ . (7)
4 Scintilla ________ vocat sed puer non respondet. (7)
5 ________ in mēnsā (on the table) est. (4)
7 Scintilla ________ iānuam it. (2)

Down

2 Scintilla ad ________ it et Horātiam vocat. (6)
3 Quīntus in ________ habitat. (6)
6 Scintilla in hortum exit ________ Horātiam vocat. (2)

CHAPTER II

(a) *Complete the following sentences by giving the correct Latin form for the words in brackets; then translate. For example:*

Quīntus agrum intrat (enters). Quintus enters the field.

1 puer Flaccum videt (sees) et vocat (calls). The boy sees Flaccus and calls him.

2 Flaccus fīlium audit (hears). Flaccus hears his son.

3 Flaccus sedet (sits) et cenam (dinner) cōnsūmit. Flaccus sits and eats dinner.

4 Flaccus puerum (the* boy) laudat; puer (the* boy) ad casam redit.

* omit 'the'

Flaccus praises the boy; the boy returns to the house.

5 Quīntus in culīnam venit (comes) et Scintillam (Scintilla) salūtat.

Quintus comes into the kitchen and greets Scintilla.

6 Scintilla non laborat (is not working) sed in culīnā sedet (is sitting).

Scintilla is not working but is sitting in the kitchen.

(b) *Pick out from the English translations below the ones that fit each of the following Latin words. (The exercise includes two verbs you have not learnt, but your knowledge of English will enable you to match them with the English translations):*

1	audit	he hears	5	vocat	she calls	9	labōrat	she is working
2	venit	he is coming	6	sedet	she is sitting	10	laudat	she praises
3	videt	he sees	7	redit	she is returning	11	respondet	he replies
4	parat	he is preparing	8	spectat	he is watching	12	salūtat	he greets

she is working **she is returning** **he is watching**
he replies **he sees** **he hears** **he is coming** **she is preparing**
she praises **she is sitting** **he greets** **she calls**

(c) *Describe in Latin what is happening in this picture:*

____

____

____

____

____

(d)

1 What would Horace's father have grown on his farm?
Would you have liked his way of life? Give reasons for your answer.

2 What do you think was the moral that the Romans drew from the story of Cincinnatus?

(e) *In this square, find and circle the Latin words that translate the words underlined below:*

1. The master calls the boy.
2. He punishes him.
3. The father ploughs the field.
4. The mother loves her son.
5. I love the girl.

A	P	P	R	O	P	I
B	P	U	E	R	U	M
P	R	E	M	A	N	A
F	I	L	I	U	M	I
Y	Z	L	T	L	O	X
N	S	A	G	R	U	M
E	U	M	C	A	N	E

(f) Which word in the following list is the odd one out: **fīliam**, **cēnam**, **iānuam**, **fīlium**, **puellam**?
Why doesn't it fit in the list?

filium - because it's the only noun that isn't feminine.

CHAPTER III

(a) *Complete the following sentences by giving the correct Latin form for the words in brackets; then translate. For example:*

Quīntus Argum vocat sed Argus nōn redit; canis malus (bad) est.

Quintus calls Argus but Argus does not come back; he's a bad dog.

1 Quīntus Argum diū quaerit; fessus (tired) est.
Quintus looks for Argus for a long time; he is tired.

2 puer sub arbore iacet et dormit (sleeps); tutus (safe) est.
The boy lies under a tree and sleeps; he is safe.

3 Scintilla filiam (her* daughter) in silvam mittit; ānxia est.
Scintilla sends her daughter into the wood; she is anxious.

* omit 'her'

4 Horātia Quintum (Quīntus) quaerit; Horātia fessa (tired) est.
Horatia looks for Quintus; Horatia is tired.

5 Horātia puerum (the** boy) videt; Horātia laeta (happy) est.
Horatia sees the boy; Horatia is happy.

** omit 'the'

6 Scintilla fīliam laudat (praises); Horātia bona (good) est.
Scintilla praises her daughter; Horatia is good.

(b) *The following words are all derived from the Latin word* **labōra–t**; *explain their meanings:*

1 **labour** work

2 **labourer** a working man

3 **laborious** involving work

4 **laboratory** somewhere you work

5 **collaborate** work together with someone

6 **elaborate** (adj.) carefully worked on

(c) *In the following phrases the adjectives (in brackets) must agree with the nouns they are describing, i.e. they must be in the same case and gender. Write in the correct form of each adjective. For example:*

bonam puellam
(bonus)

1 malum puerum (malus)
2 fīliam laetam (laetus)
3 fīlium fessum (fessus)
4 puer tutus (tūtus)
5 viam longam (longus)
6 silva obscura (obscūrus)

(d) *Describe in Latin what is happening in this picture:*

(e) *What do you suppose the following Latin words mean? (Your knowledge of English will help you):*

verbs		nouns		adjectives	
persuādet	persuades	familia	family	timidus	timid
studet	studies	fēmina	woman	sevērus	severe
ascendit	ascends	poēta	poet	squālidus	squalid
resistit	resists	lūna	moon	pallidus	pale

(f)

1 In what ways, if any, could women could have an influence in the ancient world?

2 Why couldn't Scintilla go out to work, as women do today?

3 What qualities did Roman men admire in their wives? In three or four sentences, say how you feel men's attitudes on this subject are different today.

CHAPTER IV

(a) *Complete the following sentences by giving the correct Latin form for the words in brackets; then translate. For example:*

Scintilla ___pueros___ ad agrum mittit. ___Scintilla sends the boys to the field.___
(the boys)

1 in viā puerī puellās ___vident___ . ___The boys see the girls on the road.___
(see)

2 Quīntus ___puellas___ vocat sed ___puellae___ nōn respondent.
(the girls) (the girls)
___Quintus calls the girls but the girls do not reply.___

3 puellae puerōs nōn ___audiunt___ . ___The girls do not hear the boys.___
(hear)

4 ___pueri___ clāmant et in silvās ___currunt___ .
(The boys) (run)
___The boys shout and run into the woods.___

5 puellae ___fessae___ sunt et in agrō ___manent___ .
(tired) (remain)
___The girls are tired and remain in the field.___

6 Scintilla eās ___manet___; ānxia ___est___ .
(is waiting for) (she is)
___Scintilla is waiting for them; she is anxious.___

7 tandem Scintilla puellās et ___pueros___ videt.
(the boys)
___At length Scintilla sees the girls and the boys.___

8 ad casam festīnant; valdē fessī ___sunt___ .
(they are)
___They hurry to the house; they are very tired.___

9 Scintilla eōs ___salutat___ et in casam ___ducit___ .
(greets) (leads)
___Scintilla greets them and leads them into the house.___

10 puerī in hortō sedent, sed ___puellae___ cēnam parant.
(the girls)
___The boys sit in the garden, but the girls prepare dinner.___

(b) *Pick out from the English translations below the ones that fit each of the following Latin words:*

1 festīnat	she hurries	**5** vident	they see	**9** laudant	they praise
2 manent	they remain	**6** audiunt	they hear	**10** ascendit	he is climbing
3 audit	he hears	**7** parant	they are preparing	**11** currunt	they run
4 dīcunt	they say	**8** vocat	she is calling	**12** videt	he sees

they say **he hears** **she hurries** **he is climbing**
he sees **they are preparing** **they run** **they hear** **she is calling**
they remain **they praise** **they see**

(c) *Describe in Latin what is happening in this picture:*

(d) *Form the plural of the following words:*

1 **fīlia** filiae

2 **via** viae

3 **silva** silvae

4 **fīlius** filii

5 **ager** agri

6 **puer** pueri

In English we usually form the plural of words simply by adding 's' onto their singular form. Thus 'girl' (singular) becomes 'girls' (plural).
But sometimes English words change more than that – or surprise foreigners by not changing at all.

Give the plural of:

1	**goose** geese	5	**mouse** mice
2	**sheep** sheep	6	**fish** fish
3	**ox** oxen	7	**hippopotamus** hippopotami
4	**child** children	8	**man** men

You may end up feeling that Latin plurals are less confusing than English ones can be!

(e)

1 Do you think that you would have been happy living in a Roman country town? Give your reasons.

2 You are standing for the post of **duovir** in a Roman country town. Draw a poster to boost your campaign.

(f) Have a look at the picture on page 28 of the coursebook. What is going on here? Why do you think that the women going one way have their water jugs on their sides while those going the other way have them upright?

(g) Imagine you are in a theatre: you are one of the audience sitting in the auditorium; above the door you came in by is a notice saying exit. Explain the meaning of the words underlined; to what Latin word is each related?

audience: the spectators (audio); auditorium: the room where the spectators sit (audio); exit: the way out (exeo).

The play you are watching contains several scenes performed by actors; these words too come from Latin: **scaenae**, **āctōrēs**. The Romans had theatres (**theātra**) in which plays (**fābulae**) were performed, both **tragoediae** and **cōmoediae**; what is the English form of these two words?

tragedies

comedies

A Roman theatre

CHAPTER V

(a) *Pick out from the English translations below the ones that fit each of the following Latin verb forms:*

1	spectāmus	we are watching	**6**	rogāmus	we ask	**11** festīnō	I am hurrying
2	docet	she teaches	**7**	adveniō	I arrive	**12** dīcunt	they say
3	scrībimus	we write	**8**	manētis	you remain	**13** estis	you are
4	sumus	we are	**9**	audīs	you hear	**14** facimus	we are making
5	sum	I am	**10**	currimus	we run	**15** accēdō	I approach

you (plural) are **we are making** **we are** **we write** **I am**
she teaches **I arrive** **we ask** **I am hurrying** **you (sing.) hear** **I approach**
you (plural) remain **they say** **we are watching** **we run**

(b) *Complete the following sentences by giving the correct Latin form for the words in brackets; then translate. For example:*

Quīntum salutamus . (we are greeting) — We are greeting Quintus.

1. dormit in agrō. (He is sleeping) — He is sleeping in the field.
2. cēnam paras . (you (sing.) are preparing) — You are preparing dinner.
3. Scintillam iuvo . (I am helping) — I am helping Scintilla.
4. ad lūdum ambulamus . (we are walking) — We are walking to school.
5. nōn sumus fessī. (we are) — We are not tired.
6. magister pueros vocat . (calls) — The master calls the boys.
7. puerī nōn sunt laetī. (are) — The boys are not happy.
8. in lūdō litterās scribimus . (we write) — In school we write letters.
9. cūr īrātus es , magister? (are you) — Why are you angry, Master?
10. ad lūdum sērō advenitis . (you (plural) are arriving) — You are arriving at school late.

(c) *Describe in Latin what is happening in this picture:*

____

____

____

____

____

(d) *The following Latin terms occur in connection with Roman education. What do you suppose each of them means?*

1 ēdūcō ___educate___

2 schola ___school___

3 studeō ___study___

4 scientia ___science___

5 litterae ___literature___

(*this word could also be spelt* literae)

(e) How far do you feel that we have improved on Roman education in two thousand years?

(f) *Find and circle in this square the Latin for the following:*

we love   you hear   we are   we rule
you warn   you are   they love   he is
she loves   we sit   I love

CHAPTER VI

(a) *In the following sentences put the nouns in brackets into the correct case required by the preposition and translate. The following prepositions are used in this exercise:*

ad + accusative = to | per + accusative = through | ē/ex + ablative = out of
in + accusative = into | ā/ab + ablative = from | in + ablative = in

1 māter ē casa (casa) exit. The mother goes out of the house.

2 Quīntum vocat et ad agrum (ager) mittit. She calls Quintus and sends him to the field

3 Quīntus per silvam (silva) currit et in agrum (ager) festīnat.
Quintus runs through the wood and hurries into the field.

4 pater in agro (ager) labōrat. His father is working in the field.

5 Quīntus cēnam ad patrem (pater) portat et ab agro (ager) ad casam (casa) redit.
Quintus brings a meal to his father and returns home from the field.

6 ad ludum (lūdus) accēdimus. We are going to school.

7 magister ē ianua (iānua) exit. The master comes out of the door.

8 puerōs in ludum (lūdus) vocat. He calls the boys into the school.

9 puerī in sellis (sellae) sedent. The boys sit on the chairs.

10 ā ludo (lūdus) domum festīnāmus. We hurry home from school.

(b) *Translate the following verb forms:*

1 intrō I enter
2 intrāmus we enter
3 intrant they enter
4 intrāte! enter!/come in!(plural)
5 intrās you enter (singular)
6 sedēs you sit (singular)
7 sedet he sits
8 sedē! sit! (singular)
9 sedēmus we sit
10 sedent they sit

11 scrībite!	write! (plural)	**16** venī!	come! (singular)
12 scrībunt	they write	**17** veniō	I come
13 scrībit	he writes	**18** venīmus	we come
14 scrībe!	write! (singular)	**19** venīte!	come! (plural)
15 scrībimus	we write	**20** venītis	you come

(c) *Change the following Latin phrases into the accusative case. For example:*

magna urbs magnam urbem

1 rēx fortis	rex fortem	**6** omnēs puerī	omnes pueros
2 omnēs prīncipēs	omnes principes	**7** multae nāvēs	multas naves
3 nāvis longa	navem longam	**8** bonī rēgēs	bonos reges
4 pater laetus	patrem laetum	**9** multī amīcī	multos amicos
5 bonae mātres	bonas matres	**10** pugnae terribilēs	pugnas terribiles

(d) Latin has had an enormous influence on English literature. In one of his plays, Christopher Marlowe, who lived at the same time as Shakespeare, tells the story of Doctor Faustus. Faustus is a scholar in the German university town of Wittenberg. He sells his soul to the devil in return for 24 years of total pleasure. He wins his greatest happiness when the devil summons up for him the spirit of Helen of Troy. (Another name for Troy is Ilium. That is why Homer's poem about Troy is called the *Iliad.*)

Write brief notes on each of the names underlined, saying how they fit into the story:

Faustus: Was this the face that launched a thousand ships,
And burnt the topless towers of Ilium?
Sweet Helen, make me immortal with a kiss.
I will be Paris, and for love of thee
Instead of Troy shall Wittenberg be sacked,
And I will combat with weak Menelaus,
And wear thy colours on my plumed crest.
Yea, I will wound Achilles in the heel,
And then return to Helen for a kiss.
Oh, thou art fairer than the evening's air,
Clad in the beauty of a thousand stars.

(**e**) Fābula scaenica

Persōnae: Flāvius (magister); Quīntus, Decimus, Marcus, Pūblius, Gāius, Lūcius (puerī)

Flāvius puerōs in lūdō exspectat. intrant puerī et magistrum salūtant.

puerī: salvē, magister.
Flāvius: salvēte, puerī. intrāte celeriter et sedēte.
omnēs puerī in sellīs sedent.
Flāvius: audīte, puerī. litterās scrībite. dīligenter labōrāte.
cēterī puerī labōrant, sed Gāius nōn labōrat; Quīntum calcat.
Quīntus: (*susurrat*) cūr mē calcās, Gāī? asinus es.
Gāius: (*susurrat*) tacē, Quīnte. magister nōs spectat.
Flāvius: quid facis, Gāī? cūr nōn labōrās?
Gāius: ego, magister? ego dīligenter labōrō et litterās bene scrībō.
Flāvius: venī hūc, Gāī, et dā mihi illam tabulam.
Gāius ad Flāvium adit et tabulam dat.
Gāius: vidē, magister. ego litterās bene scrībō.
Flāvius: litterās nōn bene scrībis, Gāī. ignāvus es. redī ad sellam et litterās iterum scrībe.
Gāius ad sellam redit et paulīsper labōrat.
mox duo canēs praeter lūdum currunt. Lūcius eōs per fenestram videt.
Lūcius: (*susurrat*) vidē, Marce. illī canēs in viā pugnant.
Marcus: (*susurrat*) nōn pugnant canēs; bonī sunt. sed tacē; magister nōs spectat.
Flāvius: Lūcī. cūr nōn labōrās? quid susurrās?
Lūcius: ego, magister. ego nōn susurrō sed litterās scrībō.
Flāvius: nōn vēra dīcis, Lūcī. venī hūc.
surgit Lūcius et ad magistrum adit.
Marcus: nōn Lūcius susurrat, magister, sed ego.
Flāvius: Lūcī, ad sellam redī. Marce, tacē et labōrā.
mox puella praeter lūdum ambulat; Pūblius eam spectat per fenestram.
Pūblius: (*susurrat*) vidē, Decime, puella pulchra praeter lūdum ambulat.
Decimus: (*susurrat*) puellam videō; sed illa puella Horātia est, nōn pulchra puella.
Quīntus: nōn vēra dīcis, caudex. Horātia valdē pulchra est.
Quīntus īrātus est; Decimum calcat. Decimus eum oppugnat.
Flāvius: quid facitis, puerī? malī puerī estis. sedēte et tacēte. cēterōs dīmittō, sed vōs, Quīnte et Decime, in lūdō manēte et dīligenter labōrāte usque ad vesperum.

cēterī the other
calcat kicks
susurrat whispers
bene well
dā mihi give me
ignāvus idle
paulīsper for a little
praeter past
fenestram window
vēra the truth
surgit gets up
pulchra pretty
caudex blockhead
usque ad vesperum until evening

CHAPTER VII

(a) *Translate each of the following phrases in two ways. For example:*

Horātiae māter ___the mother of Horatia___ or ___Horatia's mother___

1 Scintillae fīlius ___the son of Scintilla___ or ___Scintilla's son___

2 ager Flaccī ___the field of Flaccus___ or ___Flaccus's field___

3 īra rēgis ___the anger of the king___ or ___the king's anger___

4 nāvēs hostium ___the ships of the enemy___ or ___the enemy's ships___

5 prīncipēs Trōiānōrum ___the princes of the Trojans___ or ___the Trojans' princes___

6 puellārum cēna ___the dinner of the girls___ or ___the girls' dinner___

(b) *Put the phrases in brackets into Latin and then translate the sentences.*

1 ad iānuam ___ludi___ (of the school) vēnimus. — We came to the door of the school.

2 magister tabulās ___puerorum___ (of the boys) spectat. — The master looks at the tablets of the boys.

3 cūr in agrō ___patris___ (of father) manētis? — Why are you staying in father's field?

4 ___regis___ (the king's) nāvem quaerō. — I'm looking for the king's ship.

5 Horātia ___canum___ (the dogs') cēnam parat. — Horatia is preparing the dogs' meal.

6 īram ___magistri___ (of the master) nōn timēmus. — We are not afraid of the master's anger.

7 Trōiānī nāvēs ___Graecorum___ (of the Greeks) oppugnant. — The Trojans attack the ships of the Greeks.

8 cūr nōn iuvās ___puellae___ (the girl's) mātrem? — Why aren't you helping the girl's mother?

9 māter verba* ___filiarum___ (of her daughters) audit. — The mother listens to the words of her daughters.

10 in nāvibus ___principum___ (of the leaders) nāvigant. — They sail in the ships of the leaders.

***verba** words

(c) *In the following sentences fill the blank with an appropriate adverb from the list below.*

1 fortiter pugnāte, amīcī, et urbem capite!

2 venī huc, amīce; pater tē exspectat.

3 labōrāte diligenter, puerī; magister nōs spectat.

4 Decimus litterās male scrībit; asinus est.

5 cūr lente ambulās, Quīnte? festīnā.

dīligenter **fortiter** **male** **lentē** **hūc**

(d) *Describe in Latin what is happening in this picture. You may want to use the following Latin words:*

uxor, uxōris *f.* wife
tergum, tergī *n.* back

(e) *Put the following words into the correct list below:*

patrum **dominum** **amīcōrum** **rēgem** **ducum** **dominōrum** **equum** **puerum**

accusative singular	**genitive plural**
dominum	patrum
regem	amicorum
equum	ducum
puerum	dominorum

(f) *The list below gives Latin nouns on the left and adjectives formed from these nouns on the right. Translate each adjective by an English adjective derived from the Latin and explain its meaning. For example:*

	vir	virīlis	virile = manly
1	hostis	hostīlis	hostile = unfriendly
2	nāvis	nāvālis	naval = to do with ships
3	rēx (rēg–)	rēgālis	regal = kingly
4	prīnceps (prīncip–)	prīncipālis	principal = chief
5	nox (noct–)	nocturnus	nocturnal = in the night
6	urbs (urb–)	urbānus	urban = in the city

(g)

1 Describe the scene in the illustration on page 51 of your coursebook. How effective do you find it?

2 Who thought up the idea of the Trojan horse? What does this tell us about his character?

3 If you were given the choice of Achilles, would you choose a short life with immortal fame or a long but obscure life? Give your reasons.

(h) A Trojan priest called Laocoon warned the Trojans not to take the wooden horse left behind by the Greeks. The gods, who wanted to make sure that Troy fell, sent two hideous snakes across the sea to kill Laocoon and his sons. The grisly episode is illustrated in this statue carved in Quintus's lifetime.

Describe the look on Laocoon's face. What is the sculptor aiming to convey by the way he has carved Laocoon's muscles? Do you think that it is possible to have a pleasing statue of something horrible?

(i)

Across
3 of the girlfriends (8)
5 of the boyfriend (5)
6 of the kings = REG— (2)

Down
1 of a father (6)
2 of the walls (7)
3 of water (5)
4 of the man (4)

(j) Design a book cover for the *Iliad*, or produce a publisher's blurb and excerpts from reviews to try to ensure that the poem sells!

(k) Dialogus

Julia meets Horatia hurrying towards the woods.

Iūlia: quid facis, Horātia? cūr festīnās? exspectā mē.
Horātia: festīnō, Iūlia, quod Argum quaerō; et māter mē in casā exspectat.
Iūlia: vidē! Argus in silvam currit. vocā eum.
Horātia: venī hūc, Arge. malus canis es. redī celeriter.
Iūlia: Argus nōn redit; malus canis est.
Horātia: ego fessa sum.
Iūlia: sedē, Horātia, prope viam et exspectā eum...
quid facis, Horātia? cūr in terrā iacēs? dormīs?
Horātia: ego nōn dormiō; ecce, tē audiō.
Iūlia: vidē! ē silvā iam exit Argus et ad nōs redit.
Horātia: ō Arge, tandem redīs. bonus canis es.
Iūlia: venī, Horātia. Argum ūnā ad casam dūcimus.
Horātia: Arge, festīnā. bonus canis estō!

ūnā together
estō be!

CHAPTER VIII

(a) *Translate the following Latin verb forms:*

1 parāmus	we prepare	**11** lūdō	I play
2 parāre	to prepare	**12** lūdimus	we play
3 parant	they prepare	**13** lūdite	play! (plural)
4 parāte	prepare! (plural)	**14** lūdunt	they play
5 parātis	you prepare (plural)	**15** lūdere	to play
6 vidē	see! (plural)	**16** audītis	you hear (plural)
7 vidētis	you see (plural)	**17** audīre	to hear
8 vidēre	to see	**18** audī	hear! (singular)
9 vidēs	you see (singular)	**19** audīmus	we hear
10 vident	they see (plural)	**20** audiunt	they hear

(b) *Pick out from the English translations below the ones that fit each of the following Latin verb forms:*

1 parat	he is preparing	**8** timēmus	we fear
2 cape	take!	**9** dīcere	to say
3 īmus	we are going	**10** redit	she returns
4 parāre	to prepare	**11** iubent	they order
5 īre	to go	**12** gaudēte	rejoice!
6 sumus	we are	**13** habet	he has
7 capere	to take	**14** abīte	go away!

we are going she returns to go to take he has go away! take! we fear
they order he is preparing to say to prepare we are rejoice!

(c) *Put the phrases in brackets into the correct Latin form and translate:*

1 magister puerōs iubet celeriter intrare (to enter) et sedere (to sit down).

The master orders the boys to enter quickly and sit down.

2 puerī nōn cupiunt in lūdum ire (to go); cupiunt ludere (to play).

The boys do not want to go into the school; they want to play.

3 magister 'nōlīte lūdere, puerī,' inquit; 'dēbētis mē audire (to listen to).'

The master says, 'Don't play, boys; you ought to listen to me.'

4 puerī cōnstituunt dīligenter laborare (to work). The boys decide to work hard.

5 tandem magister cōnstituit puerōs domum mittere (to send); iubet eōs domum redire (to return).

At length the master decides to send the boys home; he orders them to return home

(d) *Describe in Latin what is happening in this picture:*

(e) *Use English words derived from the Latin words in the vocabulary list on page 60 of the coursebook to fill in the gaps. For example:*

She felt miserable when her friend was expelled.

1 Her sole claim to fame is her tennis. Otherwise she is completely untalented.

2 He was sentenced to five years' hard labour.

3 The citizens of the USA take great pride in their democratic constitution .

4 People tend to feel loyal to the country they inhabit .

(f)

1 If you were in a dangerous situation, would you like to have Odysseus as your leader? Give your reasons.

2 His **Achilles' heel** was pride. We went on a long **odyssey** to India.
What do we mean by an 'Achilles' heel' and an 'odyssey'?

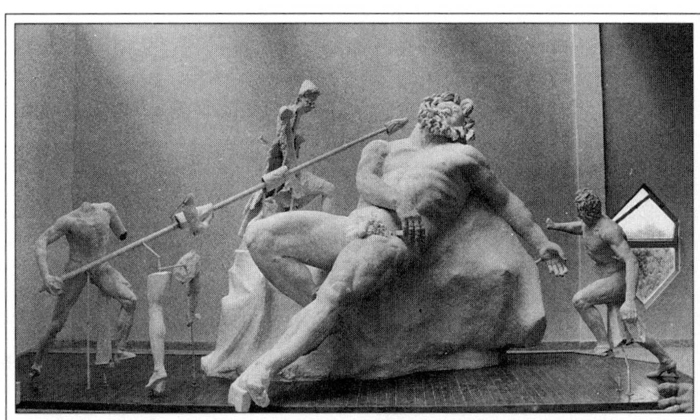

Odysseus; Odysseus and his men blinding the Cyclops; the Cyclops.

3 How do *you* imagine this one-eyed monster? Draw your own picture, or write a vivid description.

(g) Dialogus

Aeneas and his men are encamped on the shore of Sicily below Mount Etna.

Aenēās: cavēte, comitēs. quis ē silvīs ad nōs currit? vōs parāte.
Graecus: nōlīte mē oppugnāre, amīcī, vōs ōrō.
Aenēās: quis es? quid hīc facis? cūr ad nōs accēdis?
Graecus: ego Graecus sum, comes Ulixis.
Aenēās: ubi sunt comitēs tuī?
Graecus: ego sōlus sum; comitēs meī omnēs ad Graeciam nāvigant. sed fugite, miserī, fugite.
Aenēās: cūr tū nōs iubēs fugere? quid dēbēmus timēre?
Graecus: gigantēs immānēs hīc habitant. nōlīte manēre. nāvēs cōnscendite et fugite.
Aenēās: gigantēs nōn videō. nōlī nūgās nārrāre.
Graecus: ecce, gigās ingēns dē monte dēscendit.
Aenēās: dī immortālēs! gigantem iam videō. currite, comitēs. festīnāte ad nāvēs.
Graecus: nōlī mē sōlum relinquere. accipe mē in nāvem.
Aenēās: comitēs, dūcite hunc Graecum in nāvem. festīnāte. ille gigās propius accēdit.

ubi where?

nūgās nārrāre to talk nonsense

relinquere to leave

hunc this

propius too close

CHAPTER IX

(a) *Pick out from the English translations below the ones that fit each of the following Latin verb forms:*

1 sumus	we are	**6** potestis	you can	**11** abī	go away!
2 abīre	to go away	**7** redīte	go back!	**12** ades	you are present
3 possunt	they can	**8** adest	he is present	**13** redīre	to return
4 eunt	they are going	**9** exit	she goes out	**14** possumus	we can
5 adsum	I am present	**10** adsunt	they are present	**15** adeunt	they approach

they approach **we are** **they are present** **go back!** **we can**
you are present **you can** **to go away** **to return** **they can** **I am present**
go away! **she goes out** **they are going** **he is present**

(b) *Complete the following sentences by inserting in the blanks* **ubi**, **dum** *or* **quod** *as the sense requires, and translate.*

1 dum pueri lūdunt, magister ē iānuā lūdī exit.

While the boys play, the master goes out of the door of the school.

2 Horātia, ubi ad casam redit, mātrem quaerit.

When she returns to the house, Horatia looks for her mother.

3 pater īrātus est quod fīlius nōn labōrat.

The father is angry because his son isn't working.

4 Graecī, ubi Polyphēmum vident, ad nāvēs fugiunt.

When the Greeks see Polyphemus, they flee to their ships.

5 Polyphēmus Graecōs vidēre nōn potest, quod caecus est.

Polyphemus cannot see the Greeks because he is blind.

(c) *Put the following Latin phrases (i) into the accusative case, and (ii) into the genitive case. For example:*

		(i)	(ii)
	magna tempestās	magnam tempestatem	magnae tempestatis
1	senex laetus	senem laetum	senis laeti
2	tantī labōrēs	tantos labores	tantorum laborum
3	rēgīna trīstis	reginam tristem	reginae tristis
4	ingēns unda	ingentem undam	ingentis undae
5	cēterī prīncipēs	ceteros principes	ceterorum principum
6	nox longa	noctem longam	noctis longae

(d) *Describe in Latin what is happening in this picture, which shows the escape of Ulixes (the Latin name for Odysseus) from the cave of Polyphemus. You may want to use the following Latin words:*

spēlunca, spēluncae *f.* cave
observō, observāre (1) I watch, guard
sē cēlat he hides himself
sub ventre ovis under the belly of the sheep
exitus way out

____

____

____

____

(e) *From the following English sentence, give one example each of the parts of speech listed below; then translate each word you have selected into Latin:*

Aeneas told all his comrades to run to the ships. 'Flee quickly,' he shouted, 'or huge Polyphemus will get you.'

1 an imperative Flee - fugite

2 an infinitive to run - currere

3 an adjective huge - ingens

4 an adverb quickly - celeriter

5 a preposition to - ad

(f) See what you can find out about Troy as it is today. Who excavated the city and what did he discover? Your teacher will suggest some reading for you.

(g) *Tick the statements that are* **untrue:**

1 Anchīses, quī valdē senex est, perit. ☐
2 Neptūnus nūbēs dispellit et undās sēdat. ☐
3 mōns Aetna in Africā est. ☑
4 Achillēs Hectorem circum mūrōs trahit. ☐
5 rēgīna Dīdō Trōiānōs libenter accipit. ☐
6 Graecī Trōiam nōn capiunt. ☑

(h) *Circle the following in this word square:*

The name of the poem about Aeneas
The poet who wrote it
The hero whose ghost tells Aeneas to flee
The name of the Greek hero who killed him
The last king of Troy
The mother of Aeneas

S	T	A	V	B	N	A	O	T	R	L
A	C	H	I	L	L	E	S	R	O	M
H	O	M	R	V	E	N	U	S	A	N
O	V	I	G	R	H	E	C	T	O	R
R	P	R	I	A	M	I	R	A	L	S
L	A	B	L	D	E	D	L	E	M	T

(i) Dialogus

Aeneas leads his father, Anchises, his wife, Creusa, and their little son, Iulus, from the burning city of Troy.

Aenēās: hostēs accēdunt. urbs ārdet. fugere dēbēmus.
Creūsa: quō possumus īre? quōmodo possumus hostēs effugere?
Aenēās: ad montēs īmus, Creūsa. nūllī hostēs in montibus sunt.
Creūsa: hostium clāmōrēs audiō et flammae propius accēdunt. festīnāte.
Aenēās: venī hūc, pater. in umerōs meōs ascende. ego tē portābō.
Creūsa: tū, Iūle, manum patris cape.
Aenēās: et tū, Creūsa, post nōs festīnā et semper mihi prope subī. nam nox est et viam vix possumus vidēre.
Creūsa: omnēs parātī sumus. ī nunc, Aenēā.
Aenēās: venī, Iūle. fortis estō.
Creūsa: nōlī currere, Aenēā. parvus Iūlus nōn potest tam celeriter īre.
Aenēās: festīnā, Creūsa. nōn tempus est cessāre.
Creūsa: manē, Aenēā. nōlī tam celeriter īre. nōn possum vōs vidēre.

ārdet is on fire
quōmodo how?
effugere escape from
nūllī no
propius nearer
umerōs shoulders
portābō I will carry
post after
subī follow!
estō be!
cessāre to dawdle

CHAPTER X

(a) *Put the following Latin phrases into (i) the accusative, and (ii) the genitive case. For example:*

		(i)	(ii)
	omne lītus	omne litus	omnis litoris
1	flūmen magnum	flumen magnum	fluminis magni
2	altum mare	altum mare	alti maris
3	senex fortis	senem fortem	senis fortis
4	tanta perīcula	tanta pericula	tantorum periculorum
5	bonum cōnsilium	bonum consilium	boni consilii
6	multa nōmina	multa nomina	multorum nominum
7	puellae laetae	puellas laetas	puellarum laetarum
8	magna tempestās	magnam tempestatem	magnae tempestatis
9	bellum trīste	bellum triste	belli tristis
10	omnēs puerī	omnes pueros	omnium puerorum

(b) *In the following sentences put each word in brackets into the case required by the preceding preposition and translate the sentences.*

1 Trōiānī, ubi ad Siciliam (Sicilia) adveniunt, ē navibus (nāves) exeunt et in litore (lītus) sedent.

When the Trojans reach Sicily, they disembark from their ships and sit on the shore.

2 montem Aetnam vident; flammās et fūmum in caelum (caelum) prōicit.

fūmus smoke

They see Mount Aetna; it flings up flames and smoke into the sky.

3 Trōiānī timent; post cenam (cēna) prope litus (lītus) dormiunt.

The Trojans are afraid; after dinner they sleep near the shore.

4 postrīdiē Polphēmum vident; ille dē monte alto (mōns altus) cum ovibus (ovēs) lentē dēscendit.

The next day they see Polyphemus; he slowly comes down from the high mountain with his sheep.

5 Trōiānī valdē timent; Aenēās eōs iubet ad naves (nāvēs) fugere.

The Trojans are very afraid; Aeneas orders them to flee to their ships.

6 ubi ad litus (lītus) adveniunt, nāvēs cōnscendunt et ā litore (lītus) nāvigant.

When they reach the shore, they embark on their ships and sail from the shore.

7 Polyphēmus iam ad mare (mare) advenit et in undas (undae) prōcēdit.

Polyphemus now reaches the sea and goes forward into the waves.

8 nōn potest Trōiānōs vidēre sed audit eōs ā terra (terra) rēmigantēs.

rēmigantēs rowing

He cannot see the Trojans but he hears them rowing from the land.

9 saxa ingentia ē terra (terra) in naves (nāvēs) iacit.

He flings huge rocks from the land towards the ships.

10 sed Trōiānī fortiter per undas (undae) rēmigant; sīc ē periculo (perīculum) tūtī ēvādunt.

But the Trojans row strongly through the waves; thus they escape from danger safely.

(c) There are English words derived from all the words in the left-hand column of the vocabulary on page 77 of your coursebook. What are they?

amō, amāre	amiable, amatory
regō, regere	regent, regal, regicide
animus, animī	animate, animation
gladius, gladiī	gladiator
servus, servī	servile, serve

(d) Write a character sketch of Aeneas based on the impression you have got of him from these chapters.

(e) Produce a strikingly-illustrated book cover for the *Aeneid*, or an enthusiastic publisher's blurb and some quotations from rave reviews.

(f) Fābula scaenica

Persōnae: Aenēās, Faber prīmus, Faber secundus, Faber tertius, Mercurius, Trōiānus prīmus, Trōiānus secundus, Dīdō

Aenēās in lītore Libyae cessat; Carthāginem aedificat.

Aenēās: festīnāte, fabrī. saxa ad mediam urbem portāte et arcem aedificāte.

Faber prīmus: semper saxa portāmus. fessī sumus.

Aenēās: nōlīte cessāre, fabrī. dēbēmus arcem cōnficere.

Faber secundus: nōn possumus diūtius labōrāre; merīdiēs est. cupimus sub arbore iacēre et dormīre.

Aenēās: quō abītis? redīte. iubeō vōs illa saxa portāre.

Faber tertius: nōn tū nōs regis, sed Dīdō. Dīdō semper nōs iubet merīdiē dormīre.

Aenēās: abīte, hominēs, paulīsper; sed celeriter redīte et arcem cōnficite.

abeunt fabrī. Aenēās sōlus in saxō sedet. Mercurius subitō dē caelō adest et Aenēam vocat.

Mercurius: Aenēā, quid facis? cūr in lītore Libyae cessās et Dīdōnis urbem aedificās?

Aenēās: quis mē vocat? deus an homō?

Mercurius: ego Mercurius sum, nūntius deōrum. Iuppiter, pater deōrum et rēx hominum, mē mittit ad tē.

Aenēās: cūr tē mittit Iuppiter? quid mē facere iubet?

Mercurius: Iuppiter īrātus est, quod in Libyā cessās. tē iubet ad Italiam festīnāre et novam Trōiam condere.

Mercurius ēvānēscit. Aenēās territus est.

Aenēās: quid facere dēbeō? imperia deōrum nōn possum neglegere. Iuppiter omnia videt. ad comitēs festīnāre dēbeō et nāvēs parāre.

Aenēās ad comitēs festīnat.

Aenēās: audīte, comitēs. nāvēs parāte. dēbēmus statim ā Libyā nāvigāre.

Trōiānus prīmus: ō Aenēā, fessī sumus. cupimus in Libyā manēre. nōlī nōs iubēre iterum in undīs labōrāre.

Aenēās: tacē, amīce. Iuppiter ipse nōs iubet abīre; dēbēmus ad Italiam nāvigāre et novam Trōiam condere.

Trōiānus secundus: quid dīcis? Iuppiter nōs iubet novam Trōiam

faber workman
cessat delays
mediam urbem the middle of the city
arcem citadel
cōnficere to finish
diūtius any longer
merīdiēs midday
paulīsper for a little
an or?
ēvānēscit vanishes
neglegere neglect
ipse himself

in Italiā condere? gaudēte, comitēs. nec ventōs nec tempestātēs timēmus. festīnāte ad lītus et nāvēs celeriter parāte.

exeunt Trōiānī laetī. Aenēās sōlus et trīstis in lītore manet.

Aenēās: quid facere dēbeō? Dīdō mē amat. quōmodo possum eī dīcere imperia deōrum? quōmodo possum eam dēserere?

sed Dīdō omnia iam cognōvit; īrāta et misera Aenēam exspectat. ubi Aenēās advenit, fūror et īra Dīdōnis animum vincunt.

Dīdō: perfide, tū temptās tacitus abīre? neque amor meus tē retinet nec fidēs tua? mē sōlam relinquis? mē moribundam dēseris?

Aenēās: rēgīna, nōn temptō tacitus abīre; nōn cupiō tē dēserere. Mercurius ipse, nūntius deōrum, mē monet; Iuppiter mē iubet ad Italiam nāvigāre et novam Trōiam condere. nōlī mē culpāre. invītus tē relinquō. invītus Italiam petō.

Dīdō: perfide, sīc tū meās lacrimās spernis? sīc tu omnia mea beneficia rependis? ego tē nōn retineō. ī nunc. Italiam pete et novam urbem conde. sed sīc tē moneō: quod tū mē prōdis et amōrem meum spernis, ultiōnem dīram exspectā. sērius ōcius aut ego aut posterī ultiōnem dīram exigent.

Dīdō ad terram cadit exanimāta. Aenēās trīstis ad comitēs redit et nāvēs parat.

nec...nec neither...nor
quōmodo? how?
dēserere desert
cognōvit has learnt
temptās try
neque...nec neither...nor
retinet hold back
fidēs promise
relinquis leave
moribundam doomed to die
ipse himself
culpāre to blame
lacrimās tears
spernis despise
beneficia kindnesses
rependis repay
prōdis betray
ultiōnem dīram terrible vengeance
sērius ōcius sooner or later
posterī descendants
exigent will exact
cadit falls
exanimāta in a faint

CHAPTER XI

(a) *Put the following Latin phrases into the dative case:*

1	bona puella	bonae puellae
2	fīlius cārus	filio caro
3	rēx fortis	regi forti
4	tanta tempestās	tantae tempestati
5	māter misera	matri miserae
6	lītora omnia	litoribus omnibus
7	longum flūmen	longo flumini
8	flōrēs pulchrī	floribus pulchris

(b) *Pick out from the English translations below the ones that fit the following Latin verb forms:*

1	regunt	they rule
2	reddite	give back!
3	ferimus	we are carrying
4	dare	to give
5	adsumus	we are present
6	redīte	go back!
7	potest	he can
8	accipere	to receive
9	iubētis	you order
10	cōnstituunt	they decide
11	terret	he terrifies
12	ostendō	I show
13	habēmus	we have
14	gaudēte!	rejoice!
15	interficere	to kill

to kill **they decide** **they rule** **I show**
we are carrying **give back!** **he can** **to give** **to receive** **you order**
we are present **go back!** **we have** **rejoice!** **he terrifies**

(c) *In the following phrases, the words in bold type are derived from Latin words you have met. Explain their meaning in English and show how the English meaning is related to their Latin root:*

1 **undulating** hills — with a wave-like outline: unda = wave

2 **tempestuous** seas — stormy: tempestas = storm

3 **marine habitat** — natural home in the sea: habitare = to live; mare = sea

4 **ardent** lovers — passionate: ardeo = I am on fire

5 **contradictory** speeches — saying the opposite of each other: contra = against; dicere = to say

(d) *Describe in Latin what is happening in this picture:*

(e) *Read again the story of the foundation of Rome on page 87 of your coursebook. The Roman poet Ovid describes as follows how it was decided whether Romulus or Remus should be king:*

'There's no need for a fight,' said Romulus.
'We can rely on birds. Let's try what the birds say.'

rēs placet. alter adit nemorōsī saxa Palātī,
  alter Aventīnum māne cacūmen init.
sex Remus, hic volucrēs bis sex videt ordine. pāctō
  stātur. et arbitrium Rōmulus urbis habet.

rēs the plan
alter...alter the one... the other
nemorōsī of the wooded
māne in the morning
cacūmen peak
hic this man, i.e. Romulus
ordine in line
pāctō stātur they abide by their pact
arbitrium control

See whether you can translate these lines. You will have to guess **volucrēs** *and* **bis sex**.

(f) *Find and circle in the word square the Latin for the following:*

for the father
to the dogs
to the boy
to the girlfriend
to the old man
to the horses

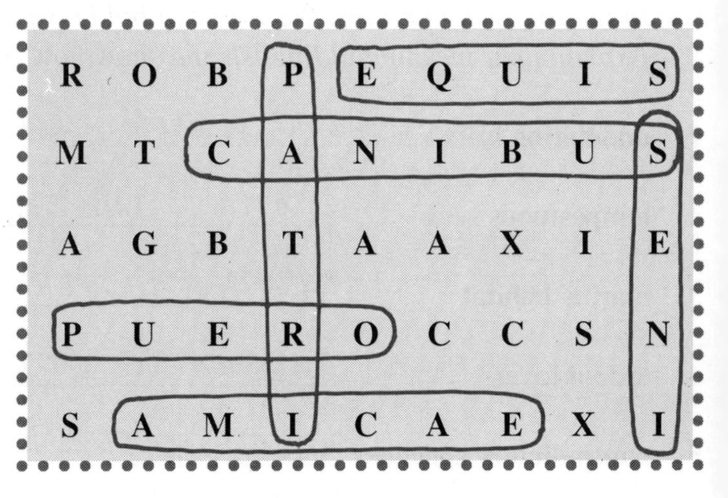

(g) Produce a cartoon strip telling the story of Romulus and Remus.

(h) Dialogus

Scintilla is returning home from the fountain.

Scintilla: dī immortālēs! quid accidit? multum fūmum videō.
Horatia comes running from the cottage.
Horātia: ō māter, venī celeriter. festīnā. casa nostra ārdet.
Scintilla: quid dīcis fīlia? fūmus ille ē casā nostrā surgit?
Horātia: ārdet casa, māter. nōlī cessāre.
Scintilla: sed Argus in casā est. canis īnfēlīx mortuus est?
Horātia: Argus tūtus est. ego eum ē casā trāxī.
Scintilla: puella fortis es. sed quid facere dēbēmus? tū, Horātia, ad agrum curre et patrī omnia nārrā.
Horātia: et tū, māter, ad casam festīnā vīcīnōsque vocā.
Scintilla: dī immortālēs! mea culpa est. pater valdē īrātus erit.
Horātia: cāra māter, nōlī cessāre. curre ad casam et Argum cūrā. prope viam iacet semimortuus.
Scintilla: ō Arge, ō canis īnfēlīx! mea culpa est.

accidit is happening
īnfēlīx unhappy
trāxī I dragged
vīcīnōs neighbours
erit will be
cūrā look after

CHAPTER XII

(a) *Write out the following phrases in all cases.*

	1 **puella trīstis** (singular)	2 **pater bonus** (singular)	3 **lītora omnia** (plural)
nom.	puella tristis	pater bonus	litora omnia
acc.	puellam tristem	patrem bonum	litora omnia
gen.	puellae tristis	patris boni	litorum omnium
dat.	puellae tristi	patri bono	litoribus omnibus
abl.	puella tristi	patre bono	litoribus omnibus

(b) *Study the reflexive verb* ego mē lavō *on page 93 of your coursebook, and write out a similar chart for* ego mē vertō:

ego me verto	nos nos vertimus
tu te vertis	vos vos vertitis
ille se vertit	illi se vertunt

(c) *Answer the questions below on the following passage:*

Argus malus canis est; in lūtō sē volvit et valdē sordidus est. Scintilla Horātiam vocat et 'venī hūc, Horātia,' inquit; 'Argus valdē sordidus est; necesse est eum lavāre. Quīntum vocā; dēbet ille tē iuvāre.' Quīntus ubi advenit, 'ō Arge,' inquit, 'ō canis sordide, cūr tū nōn potes tē lavāre? ego nōn cupiō tē lavāre.' sed Scintilla 'festīnāte, puerī,' inquit; 'vōs parāte.' Quīntus Argum in hortum dūcit; Horātia urnam aquae portat; sed ubi sē vertit, Argus non adest. in viam fūgit; nam nōn cupit lavārī.

lūtō mud
volvit he rolls
sordide dirty
necesse est it is necessary

fūgit has fled
lavārī to be washed

1 How is Argus naughty? He rolls in the mud and gets very dirty. (2)

2 What does Scintilla tell Horatia to do? To call Quintus so that both he and Horatia can wash Argus. (4)

3 What does Quintus ask Argus? Why can't he wash himself? (2)

4 When Horatia brings the water, where is Argus? and why? He is in the road because he doesn't want to be washed. (2)

5 List and translate the four examples of verbs used in this passage with reflexive pronouns.

se volvit = rolls himself; te lavare = to wash yourself; vos parate = prepare yourselves, get ready; se vertit = turns round. (8)

(d) *Describe in Latin what is happening in the picture on page 90 of the coursebook. You may want to use the following Latin words:*

oppidānī the townspeople
imperātor the general
vectus riding

(e) *The Latin word* castra *became changed in English to* Chester. *The names of many English towns end with –chester. These are places where the Roman legions camped. Give the names of five English towns with this ending.*

Chichester, Colchester, Manchester, Rochester, Winchester and Chester among others.

(f) *Show how the words in bold type are related to the Latin* prīmus*:*

1 **Prime** Minister — the Queen's first (i.e. chief) minister

2 The **Primate** of all England (the Archbishop of Canterbury) — the head (i.e. first man) of the Church of England

3 **primates** (animals) — the highest (i.e. first) class of mammals

4 **primary** education — the first stage of compulsory education

5 his **prime** motive — chief, most important

See if you can find any more words derived from prīmus *in your English dictionary.*

prima donna, primal, primer, primeval, primitive, etc.

(g) Choose one of the great Roman gods (see page 96 and look back to page 48 in your coursebook) and see what you can find out about him or her. Draw a picture of the one you choose – complete with his or her props.

(h) Dialogus

Quintus and Gaius are watching the soldiers.

Quīntus: venī, Gāī, ad illum collem. ex eō mīlitēs spectāre possumus.
Gāius: vidē, Quīnte. quid faciunt mīlitēs?
Quīntus: imperātor manum tollit. omnēs mīlitēs cōnsistunt.
Gāius: ecce, mīlitēs iam castra pōnunt. quam celeriter opera faciunt!
Quīntus: cavē, Gāī. duo mīlitēs ad nōs accēdunt. dēbēmus nōs cēlāre.
Gāius: nōlī tē vexāre. mīlitēs iam ad castra redeunt.
Quīntus: nox adest. sine dubiō parentēs ānxiī sunt et īrātī.
Gāius: dēbēmus domum festīnāre. venī, Quīnte. nōlī cessāre.
Quīntus: nox obscūra est. vix possum viam vidēre.
Gāius: umbrās timeō. iuvā mē, Quīnte.
Quīntus: fortis estō, Gāī. manum meam cape. nōn longē abest oppidum. ecce, portās vidēre possum.

imperātor the general
tollit is raising
cōnsistunt halt
cavē look out!
cēlāre to hide
vexāre to worry
sine dubiō without doubt
umbrās the shadows

Soldiers from Trajan's column

CHAPTER XIII

(a) *Write out (i) the imperfect tense of* **dīcō** *and (ii) the perfect tense of* **parō**.

(i) dicebam, dicebas, dicebat, dicebamus, dicebatis, dicebant

(ii) parabam, parabas, parabat, parabamus, parabatis, parabant

(b) *Translate the following verb forms:*

1	spectā	look! (sing.)	**7**	dūcēbas	you were leading (sing.)	**13** dormīre	to sleep
2	spectābam	I was looking	**8**	dūcere	to lead	**14** dormī	sleep! (sing.)
3	spectat	he looks	**9**	dūcunt	they lead	**15** dormiēbant	they were sleeping
4	spectāvī	I looked	**10**	dūxistis	you led (plur.)	**16** dormīvistī	you slept (sing.)
5	spectāre	to look	**11**	dūcite	lead! (plur.)	**17** dormiō	I sleep
6	spectāvērunt	they looked	**12**	dūcimus	we lead	**18** dormiēbāmus	we were sleeping

(c) *Note that the stem of* **eō** *is* **i**-; *hence infinitive* **ī-re**, *imperfect* **ī-bam**, *perfect* **i-ī**. *Translate the following verb forms:*

1	redībam	I was returning	**4**	init	he enters	**7**	exeunt	they go out
2	redīte	return! (plur.)	**5**	iniit	he entered	**8**	exīre	to go out
3	rediit	he returned	**6**	inīre	to enter	**9**	exiērunt	they went out

(d) *In the following sentences put each verb in brackets into the appropriate tense (imperfect or perfect) and translate. For example:*

Horātia Quīntusque in hortō ludebant (lūdere), cum Scintilla eōs vocavit (vocāre).

Horatia and Quintus were playing in the garden when Scintilla called them.

1 Scintilla puerōs ad agrum misit (mittere); iussit eōs cēnam patrī portāre.

Scintilla sent the children to the field; she told them to carry a meal to their father.

2 puerī lentē per silvam _ambulabant_ (ambulāre), cum lupum vīdērunt.

The children were walking slowly through the wood when they saw a wolf.

3 Horātia valdē _timebat_ (timēre), sed Quīntus _clamavit_ (clāmāre); lupus fūgit.

Horatia was very frightened, but Quintus shouted; the wolf fled.

4 tandem puerī agrum _intraverunt_ (intrāre) patremque _vocaverunt_ (vocāre).

At length the children entered the field and called their father.

5 ille puerōs nōn _audivit_ (audīre); nam nōn _laborabat_ (labōrāre) sed sub arbore _dormiebat_ (dormīre).

He did not hear the children; for he was not working but sleeping under a tree.

6 Argus prope eum _iacebat_ (iacēre); ubi puerōs vīdit, laetus _latravit_ (latrāre = to bark).

Argus was lying near him; when he saw the children, he barked happily.

7 Argus Flaccum _excitavit_ (excitāre = to wake); ille puerōs _salutavit_ (salūtāre).

Argus woke Flaccus up; he greeted the children.

8 puerī cēnam patrī trādidērunt Argumque domum _duxerunt_ (dūcere).

trādidērunt handed over

The children handed over the meal to their father and led Argus home.

(e) *Describe in Latin what is happening in this picture:*

(f) *Italian, Spanish and French are called Romance languages, that is languages directly descended from the language of the Romans (Latin). To the chart below add (i) the corresponding Latin word on the left and (ii) the English translation on the right:*

Latin	Italian	Spanish	French	English
filius	figlio	hijo	fils	son
amicus	amico	amigo	ami	friend
ventus	vento	viento	vent	wind
vinum	vino	vino	vin	wine
murus	muro	muro	mur	wall
filia	figlia	hija	fille	daughter
tempestas	tempesta	tempestad	tempête	storm
festa (dies)	festa	fiesta	fête	festival
amare	amare	amar	aimer	love
movere	movere	mover	mouvoir	move
vivere	vivere	vivir	vivre	live
dormire	dormire	dormir	dormir	sleep

1 Which modern language appears to be most closely related to Latin? Italian

2 Which of the nouns (the first eight rows) are masculine and which are feminine (there is no neuter gender in Italian, Spanish or French)?

masculine: words for son, friend, wind, wall and wine (neuter in Latin);

feminine: words for daughter, storm and festival.

3 What is the significance of the sign ^ in French? an 's' in the Latin has disappeared.

(g) Dialogus

Flaccus and Scintilla discuss what to do about Quintus's schooling.

Flaccus: cūr Quīntus ā lūdō tam mātūrē rediit, Scintilla?
Scintilla: tumultus in lūdō factus est. Decimus magistrum oppugnāvit. omnēs puerī domum fūgērunt.
Flaccus: dī immortālēs! scelestī sunt illī puerī et magister est asinus. quid facere dēbēmus? Quīntus nihil discit in illō lūdō.
Scintilla: vērum dīcis, Flacce. Quīntus valdē ingeniōsus est sed nihil discit.
Flaccus: ignāvus est; cēterī puerī eum in malōs mōrēs dūcunt.
Scintilla: Flacce, Quīntus dēbet Rōmam īre. dēbēmus eum ad optimum lūdum mittere.
Flaccus: dī immortālēs! quid dīcis, uxor? nōn potest Quīntus Rōmam sōlus īre.
Scintilla: vērum dīcis, Flacce; sōlus Quīntus nōn potest īre; tū dēbēs eum Rōmam dūcere.
Flaccus: nōlī nūgās nārrāre, uxor. non possum vōs relinquere; nōn possum agrum neglegere. Rōma longissimē abest.
Scintilla: nōlī tē vexāre, Flacce. crās rem iterum disserēmus. iam tempus est dormīre.

mātūrē early
factus est occurred
ingeniōsus clever
ignāvus idle
mōrēs habits
nūgās nārrāre talk nonsense
longissimē very far
vexāre worry
crās tomorrow
disserēmus we shall discuss

(h) How do the characters of Flaccus and Scintilla come across in (g)?

The road to Rome, the Appian Way

CHAPTER XIV

(a) *Translate the following verb forms:*

1 vocant they call
2 vocāvistī you called (sing.)
3 vocāre to call
4 vocābās you were calling
5 vocāte call! (plur.)
6 vocāvī I called
7 mittēbāmus we were sending
8 mittunt they send
9 mīsimus we sent
10 mittite send! (plur.)
11 mīsistis you sent (plur.)
12 mittere to send
13 movēre to move
14 mōvit he moved
15 movet he moves
16 movēbam I was moving
17 movēte move! (plur.)
18 mōvērunt they moved

(b) *Translate the following sentences; be sure you translate all perfect tenses appropriately, choosing between the two possible meanings, e.g.* parāvī = *I prepared* or *I have prepared.*

(Note the following: eō, īre, iī; redeō, redīre, rediī; abeō, abīre, abiī*)*

1 Quīntus per silvām festīnābat; Argum quaerēbat.

Quintus was hurrying through the wood; he was looking for Argus.

2 Flaccus ab agrō redībat, cum fīlium in silvā vīdit.

Flaccus was returning from the field when he saw his son in the wood.

3 Flaccus eum vocāvit; 'quid facis, fīlī?' inquit; 'cūr domō discessistī?'

Flaccus called him; 'What are you doing, son?' he said; 'Why have you left home?'

4 Quīntus 'māter' inquit 'mē mīsit in silvam. nam Argus in silvam abiit. ego eum quaerō sed nōn invēnī.'

Quintus said, 'Mother sent me into the wood. For Argus has gone off into the wood. I'm looking for him but haven't found him.'

5 Flaccus respondit: 'nōlī tē vexāre, fīlī. sine dubiō domum iam rediit.'

Flaccus replied, 'Don't worry, son. Without doubt he has already gone back home.'

6 domum ambulābant pater et fīlius, cum Argum vīdērunt.

Father and son were walking home when they saw Argus.

7 Argus Quīntum prope viam exspectābat; ubi eōs vīdit, laetus ad Quīntum cucurrit. *Argus was waiting for Quintus near the road; when he saw them, he ran happily to Quintus.*

8 Flaccus 'Arge,' inquit, 'cūr domō abiistī? malus canis es. Quīntum valdē vexāvistī.'

Flaccus said, 'Argus, why did you go away from the house? You are a bad dog. You have worried Quintus very much.'

(c) *Describe in Latin what is happening in this picture:*

(d) In English we almost always use Arabic numbers, but sometimes, for example on some clock faces and at the end of BBC television programmes, you will see Roman numbers. They go like this:

ūnus	I	sex	VI
duo	II	septem	VII
trēs	III	octō	VIII
quattuor	IV (or IIII)	novem	IX
quīnque	V	decem	X

You should be able to see how IV can be four. Explain why VI is six and IX is nine.

I after another number is added to it: 5+1=6.

I before another number is subtracted from it: 10-1=9.

What are the Arabic equivalents of the following numbers?

XIV 14 XXIII 23 XXXIX 39

(e) The Roman Empire eventually collapsed, but the Latin language survived where the Romans had been longest. You could gather from 13(f) how close to Latin many French, Spanish and Italian words are. But the Latin language spread far wider than France, Spain and Italy. Of course, it has changed a great deal over the years, but you can see from the following chart how similar the words for one to ten are in this family of 'Romance' languages:

	Latin	Italian	Spanish	French	Portuguese	Romanian
1	ūnus	uno	uno	un	um	un
2	duo	due	dos	deux	dois	doi
3	trēs	tre	tres	trois	três	trei
4	quattuor	quattro	cuatro	quatre	quarto	patru
5	quīnque	cinque	cinco	cinq	cinco	cinci
6	sex	sei	seis	six	seis	şase
7	septem	sette	siete	sept	sete	şapte
8	octō	otto	ocho	huit	oito	opt
9	novem	nove	nueve	neuf	nove	noua
10	decem	dieci	diez	dix	dez	zece

Divide into pairs. Imagine that you and your partner are judges of the Eurovision song contest. Award marks between one and ten to each country in the chart – yes, Romania and Ancient Rome have been allowed to enter – in its own language. Then see if your partner can put your marks into English.

(f) *Which is the odd word out in the following four lists and why?*

1 nāvis, flūmen, collis, canālis, aqua — collis, a hill (all the others are to do with water) or aqua is a 1st declension noun (all the others are 3rd)

2 malus, audāx, saevus, bonus, scelestus — audax is a 3rd declension adj. (all the others are 2nd)

3 nox, lūna, umbra, clārus, sōl — clarus is an adjective (all the others are nouns)

4 lupus, nauta, canis, leporēs, culicēs — nauta, a sailor (he is the only human)

(g) *What is:*

1 a **lunar** eclipse — an eclipse of the moon

2 the **solar** system — the sun and all the planets that revolve around it

3 a **nautical** almanac — a calendar for use at sea

4	a **local** newspaper	a paper for a particular region
5	a **civic** reception	a party given by local government officers
6	an **arboreal** ape	an ape which lives in trees
7	an **itinerant** circus	a travelling circus
8	a **translucent** stone	a stone through which light can shine
9	a **tertiary** education	the third stage of education, e.g. at a university
10	a string **quartet**	a group of four string-players

(h) Dialogus

Flaccus and Quintus are sleeping in a wood beside the road to Rome.

Quīntus: pater, lupōs audiō. nōn tūtī sumus in silvā.
Flaccus: nōlī timēre, fīlī. lupī longē absunt, neque hūc accēdere audent; nam ignem timent.
Quīntus: audī pater; lupōs iterum audīvī. nōn longē absunt.
Flaccus: dormī, fīlī. ego tē cūrābō.

A few hours later…

Flaccus: (*susurrat*) Quīnte, surge celeriter sed tacitus estō. venī mēcum.
Quīntus: cūr mē in virgulta dūcis, pater? quid accidit?
Flaccus: trēs hominēs accēdunt. vīdī eōs et vōcēs audīvī. dēbēmus nōs cēlāre.
Quīntus: (*susurrat*) ecce, pater, hominēs ad ignem accēdunt. quid faciunt?
Flaccus: tacē, Quīnte, hominēs tē audient.
Quīntus: pater, hominēs impedimenta nostra rapiunt. quid facere dēbēmus?
Flaccus: tacē, Quīnte. in magnō perīculō sumus.
Quīntus: iam abeunt hominēs. tandem tūtī sumus.
Flaccus: vērum dīcis, fīlī. hominēs abiērunt. sed nōlī ē virgultīs īre. dēbēmus hīc dormīre, cēlātī.

cūrābo I shall look after
surge get up!
estō be
virgulta undergrowth
accidit has happened
cēlāre hide
audient will hear
impedimenta baggage
cēlātī hidden

CHAPTER XV

(a) *Form the imperfect, perfect, and pluperfect tenses (1st person singular) of the following verbs and translate each verb form. For example:*

regō regebam: I was ruling, rexi: I ruled or I have ruled, rexeram: I had ruled

1 servō servabam: I was saving; servavi: I saved; servaveram: I had saved

2 terreō terrebam: I was frightening; terrui: I frightened; terrueram: I had frightened

3 dīcō dicebam: I was speaking; dixi: I spoke; dixeram: I had spoken

4 dormiō dormiebam: I was sleeping; dormivi: I slept; dormiveram: I had slept

5 redeō redibam: I was returning; redii: I returned; redieram: I had returned

(b) *Pick out from the English translations below the ones that fit the following Latin verb forms:*

1 mīsī I sent

2 mōvērunt they moved

3 stābam I was standing

4 dūcis you are leading

5 flēbant they were weeping

6 rediērunt they returned

7 nārrābat he was relating

8 didicistī you learnt

9 vīxerāmus we had lived

10 abīte! go away!

11 mittō I am sending

12 erāmus we were

13 pōnunt they place

14 contendēbāmus we were marching

15 monuimus we have warned

16 dūxērunt they led

17 dare to give

18 audīverātis you had heard

they place **I sent** **to give** **we have warned** **you are leading** **go away!** **I am sending** **they moved** **I was standing** **you learnt** **we were marching** **they returned** **they led** **you had heard** **we had lived** **we were** **they were weeping** **he was relating**

(c) In your activities for the last two chapters, you saw how Latin was the parent of what we call Romance languages. But Latin itself is a member of a far wider family of languages. We have lost the parent of these languages, but we call it Indo-European (see page 4 of your coursebook).

Now have a look at the chart on the next page. In each column, each word means the same thing.

Sanscrit	pitar	matar	bhratar	svasar
Greek	pater	meter	phrater	heor
Latin	pater	mater	frater	soror
German	Vater	Mutter	Bruder	Schwester
Anglo-Saxon	faeder	modor	brothor	sweostor
Russian		mat'	brat	siestra
Irish	athair	mathair	brathair	
English	father	mother	brother	sister
French	père	mère	frère	soeur

See if you can fill in the English and French equivalents for these words. Do the English or the French words seem closer to most of the languages in the chart?

The English are closer.

(d) *Explain the meaning of the words in bold type with reference to the Latin word* **oculus***:*

1 I visited the **oculist**. the person who treats eyes.

2 He gave me an **ocular** demonstration of the truth of what he claimed.

visual – I could see his demonstration.

3 He was wearing a **monocle**. an eyeglass for one eye.

4 She was using **binoculars**. a kind of telescope used by both eyes at once.

(e) Choose one of the buildings of Ancient Rome that Quintus has passed on page 120 of your coursebook (see also page 126) and see what more you can find out about it. You may be persuaded to give a short talk to your form – with illustrations!

(f) Fābula scaenica

Persōnae: Flaccus, Quīntus, cīvis, iānitor.

Flaccus Quīntusque per viās urbis festīnant.

Flaccus: festīnā, Quīnte. nōlī tam lentē ambulāre.
Quīntus: exspectā mē, pater; nōn possum celerius īre. numquam tantam turbam hominum vīdī. nōn possum per turbam prōcēdere.
Flaccus: venī hūc, fīlī. ego tē exspectō. ecce, manum meam cape.
Quīntus: cavē, pater. ille homō paene tē ē viā dētrūsit.
Flaccus: quid facis, caudex? paene mē ē viā detrūsistī.
cīvis: quid dīcis, rūstice? nōlī mē sīc vituperāre. cēde mihi.
Flaccus: homo impudēns es et petulāns. nōn cēdam tibi.
cīvis: quid dīcis? mē impudentem vocās et petulantem? nōn mihi cēdis? cavē.
Flaccus: venī mēcum celeriter, Quīnte. nōlī caudicem illum audīre. paene ad Subūram advēnimus. iam domicilium quaerere dēbēmus.
Quīntus: ecce, pater, nōnne vidēs illam īnsulam? certē possumus domicilium illīc invenīre.
Quīntus Flaccusque īnsulam intrant et iānitōrem quaerunt.
Flaccus: Quīnte, dēbēmus iānitōrem invenīre. iānitor, ubi es? venī hūc. domicilium condūcere volō.
Quīntus: iānitor nihil nōbis respondet, pater. ubi est? dēbēmus eum quaerere. ecce, videō eum. in illō angulō dormit.
Flaccus ad angulum aulae accēdit et iānitōrem vocat.
Flaccus: surge, iānitor, et nōbīs respondē. ego fīliusque nūper Rōmam advēnimus. domicilium condūcere volumus.
iānitor: nūllum domicilium est vacuum. abīte.
Quīntus: iānitor ēbrius est, pater. quid facere dēbēmus?
Flaccus: audī mē, iānitor, nōn magnum domicilium rogāmus. nōnne ūnum cēnāculum habēs vacuum?
iānitor: nōnne audīvistī, caudex? nullum cēnāculum habeō vacuum. ego dormīre cupiō. abīte, abīte.
iānitor iterum dormit. Flaccus Quīntusque in viam exeunt.
iānitor: cōnsistite. manēte. ego errāvī. ūnum cēnāculum parvum habeō vacuum.
Flaccus: surge, iānitor, et duc nōs ad cēnāculum.

celerius quicker
cavē look out!
dētrūsit pushed
vituperāre abuse
cēde give way to
petulāns rude
cēdam I shall give way to
domicilium a flat
certē surely
ubi? where?
condūcere to rent
volō I want
angulō corner
aulae courtyard
surge get up
nūper lately
vacuum empty
ēbrius drunk
cēnāculum garret
cōnsistite stop
errāvī I was wrong

CHAPTER XVI

(a) *Write out the accusative, genitive, dative and ablative cases of:*

(i) vultus sēvērus (singular)

vultum severum

vultus severi

vultui severo

vultu severo

(ii) omnēs exercitūs (plural)

omnes exercitus

omnium exercituum

omnibus exercitibus

omnibus exercitibus

(b) *Complete the following sentences by putting the word in brackets into the correct Latin form, and then translate.*

1 cēterī puerī iam in aulā ludebant (were playing), sed Quīntus prope iānuam sōlus stabat (was standing).

The rest of the boys were now playing in the courtyard, but Quintus was standing alone by the door.

2 Orbilius ē iānuā exiit (came out) et 'intrāte celeriter, puerī,' inquit; 'tempus est studere (to study).'

Orbilius came out of the door and said, 'Come in quickly, boys, it's time to study.'

3 Orbilius Iliadem Hōmerī docebat (was teaching); multōs versūs celeriter recitavit (he recited).

Orbilius was teaching the Iliad of Homer; he quickly recited many verses.

4 'Quīnte,' inquit, 'responde (answer!) mihi. nōnne potes (can you) intellegere illōs versūs?'

'Quintus,' he said, 'answer me. Can't you understand those verses?'

5 Quīntus respondit: 'nōn possum (I can) illōs versūs intellegere, magister; nam eōs celeriter recitavisti (you recited).'

Quintus replied: 'I cannot understand those verses, master; for you recited them quickly.'

6 cēterī puerī riserunt (laughed), sed Orbilius īrātus fuit (was) et 'tacēte, puerī,' inquit; 'cūr ridetis (are you laughing) ? tū, Quīnte, mē dīligenter audi (listen to) .'

The rest of the boys laughed, but Orbilius was angry and said, 'Be quiet, boys; why are you laughing? You, Quintus, listen to me carefully.'

7 Orbilius versūs iterum recitavit (recited) ; Quīntus omnia iam intellegere potuit (was able) .

Orbilius recited verses again; Quintus was now able to understand everything.

8 tandem Orbilius puerōs dimisit (dismissed) ; cēterī iam exierant (had gone out), cum Orbilius Quīntum revocavit (called back) . At length Orbilius dismissed the boys; the rest had already gone out, when Orbilius called Quintus back.

9 'veni (come) hūc, Quīnte,' inquit; 'nōlī dēsperāre; dīligenter studes (you are studying) et celeriter discis (you are learning) .' 'Come here, Quintus,' he said; 'don't despair; you are studying hard and you are learning quickly.'

10 Quīntus Orbilium valēre iussit et laetus exiit (went out) .

Quintus said goodbye to Orbilius and went out happily.

(c) *Describe in Latin what is happening in this picture:*

(d) In the following school report explain the meaning of the words in bold print. See if you can track down their Latin roots (in other words, can you find out how the Latin and English words are related to each other):

Julia is a good **student**. She shows considerable **facility** for natural **science** and makes good use of the **library**. She does not show much **manual** dexterity in the **laboratory** but is **gradually** improving; her efforts there are not to be **derided**.

student: someone who studies (studeo = I study); facility: ability (facilis = easy); science: the study of chemistry, etc. (scio = I know); library: a room containing books (liber = book); manual: with her hands (manus = hand); laboratory: a room or building used for experiments (labor = work); gradually: step by step (gradus = step); derided: laughed at (rideo = I laugh)

(e) We live in a democracy. But there are ways in which we are in fact far from democratic. What are they? How much say do your parents – or you, for that matter – have on any individual issue?

(f) Dialogus

Quintus is going home with Flaccus after his first day at the school of Orbilius.

Flaccus: cūr trīstis es, fīlī? bene studuistī; Orbilius tē laudāvit.
Quīntus: ō pater, Orbilius valdē sevērus est. īrātus erat quod Graecē dīcere nōn poteram.
Flaccus: nōlī dēspērāre, fīlī. iam litterās Graecās discis et mox poteris Graecē dīcere.
Quīntus: cēterī puerī omnia sciunt, ego nihil. mē rīdēbant quod tam ignārus eram.
Flaccus: sed ingeniōsus es, fīlī, et dīligenter studēs. discere cupis. mox omnēs superābis.
Quīntus: ō pater, cēterī puerī lautī sunt et magnī, ego parvus et pinguis.
Flaccus: nōlī nūgās nārrāre; nōn valdē pinguis es.
Quīntus: ubi Orbilius nōs in aulam dīmīsit, nēmō mēcum lūdēbat. sōlus in angulō aulae stābam.
Flaccus: nōn vērum dīcis, fīlī. puerōrum quīdam tēcum loquēbātur. ego ipse vīdī.
Quīntus: vērum dīcis, pater. ille puer cōmis erat.
Flaccus: mox multōs amīcōs inter puerōs habēbis. nōn malī puerī sunt. nōlī dēspērāre. ecce, ad īnsulam nostram advēnimus. ego cēnam magnificam tibi parāvī. festīnā, et bonō animō estō.

poteris you will be able
ignārus ignorant
superābis you will beat
lautī smart
pinguis fat
nūgās nārrāre talk nonsense
aulam courtyard
angulō corner
quīdam one
loquēbātur was talking
ipse (my)self
cōmis kind
habēbis you will have
bonō animō estō cheer up

CHAPTER XVII

(a) *Pick out from the adjectives below the ones that agree with each of the following nouns. The adjective must be in the same case, gender and number as the noun, and the resulting phrase must make sense. For example,* **vōce omne** *is wrong, because* **vōce** *is ablative feminine singular, and* **omne** *is nominative or accusative neuter singular, nor does the phrase* **vōce omne** *make sense.*

1 bellum omne

2 puellae pulchrae

3 vōce magna

4 vultū gravi

5 nōmina clara

6 iuvenem audacem

7 cīvium bonorum

8 arboris altae

altae **clāra** **gravī** **audācem** **bonōrum** **pulchrae** **magnā** **omne**

(b) *Translate the following verb forms:*

1 cōnfēcerant they had finished

2 cōnficite finish! (plur.)

3 cōnfēcī I (have) finished

4 cōnficere to finish

5 cōnficiēbas you were finishing

6 redīre to return

7 redeunt they return

8 redībat he was returning

9 rediistī you (have) returned

10 redī return! (sing.)

11 emit he buys

12 emēbātis you were buying (plur.)

13 ēmistis you (have) bought (plur.)

14 ēmit he (has) bought

15 ēmerant they had bought

(c) *Give the accusative, genitive, dative and ablative of:*

(i) **fīlia cāra**

filiam caram

filiae carae

filiae carae

filiā cara

(ii) **victor saevus**

victorem saevum

victoris saevi

victori saevo

victore saevo

(d) *Describe in Latin what is happening in this picture:*

(e) What happens if you meet with **insuperable** obstacles? You cannot overcome them.

What is **oratory**? The art of making speeches.

Why is a **pedestrian** so called? He is on foot.

When do you use your **vocal** chords? When you use your voice.

What is a lengthy **epistle**? A long letter.

(f)

1 What, if anything, do you find ridiculous in the line of Cicero's poetry quoted on page 143 of your coursebook? (You may choose to defend it!)

2 Do you fancy the idea of a career in politics? Give reasons for your answer.

(g) Dialogus

Cicero asks Quintus what he has done in school.

Cicerō: venī hūc, Quīnte. vērumne dīxit Marcus? tū ingeniōsus es? tu cēterōs puerōs studiīs superās?
Quīntus: nōn valdē ingeniōsus sum neque omnēs aliōs superō. sed discere cupiō et studiīs gaudeō.
Cicerō: euge, Quīnte. dīc mihi, quid in lūdō hodie didicistī?
Quīntus: ante merīdiem Orbilius Iliadem Homērī docēbat.
Cicerō: cuī partī Iliadis studēbātis, Quīnte?

euge good!

cuī partī which part

Quīntus: librō sextō studēbāmus, Cicerō, in quō Hector cum uxōre loquitur et cum parvō fīliō.
Cicerō: placuit tibi haec fābula?
Quīntus: mihi valdē placuit. fābula et pulchra est et trīstis.
Cicerō: cūr trīstis est haec fābula?
Quīntus: quod et Hector et uxor hoc sciunt: mox Hector in pugnā cadet. sic fāta dēcernunt.
Cicerō: euge, Quīnte. certē puer ingeniōsus es Homērumque bene intellegis. sī vīs, licet tibi librōs meōs legere. Marce, dūc Quīntum ad bibliothēcam et ostende eī meōs librōs.
Quīntus: grātiās tibi agō, Cicerō. valdē cōmis fuistī.

in quō in which
loquitur talks
placuit tibi pleased you
haec this
cadet will fall
fāta the fates
dēcernunt decree
sī vīs if you like
licet tibi you may
bibliothēcam library
cōmis kind

A young Roman with his scroll and satchel

CHAPTER XVIII

(a) Note how Latin nouns can be formed from adjectives; for example:

audāx (audāc–is) bold, rash: **audācia** boldness, rashness
līber–a–um free: **lībertās, lībertātis** freedom

From the adjectives in the first column, deduce the meanings of the nouns in the second column:

1	dīligēns	dīligentia	carefulness, care
2	trīstis	trīstitia	sadness
3	laetus	laetitia	happiness
4	gravis	gravitās	heaviness, seriousness
5	sevērus	sevēritās	severity, harshness
6	celer	celeritās	speed

(b) *Pick out from the English translations below the ones that fit the following Latin verb forms:*

1	posueram I had placed	7	lēgistis you have read	13	agēbam I was doing
2	cognōvī I have learnt	8	superāveras you had overcome	14	vendidī I sold
3	īnspiciunt they look at	9	audēbam I was daring	15	dā give!
4	superāvimus we have overcome	10	stābam I was standing	16	movē move!
5	ēgerāmus we had done	11	invēnimus we found	17	movēbam I was moving
6	legitis you are reading	12	invenimus we find	18	dedērunt they gave

you have read **I sold** **they look at** **you had overcome** **give!** **I was doing**
we have overcome **we found** **I was daring** **they gave** **I had placed** **I was moving**
we find **you are reading** **move!** **I have learnt** **we had done** **I was standing**

(c) *Put the phrases in brackets into the correct case and translate:*

1 prima luce Quīntus cum patre domo discessit.
(prīma lūx) (pater) (domus)
At dawn Quintus left the house with his father.

2 lūdus Orbiliī foro nōn longē aberat; brevi tempore ad lūdum advēnerant.
(forum) (breve tempus)
Orbilius's school was not far from the forum; in a short time they had come to the school.

3 amīcī, ubi Quīntum cōnspexērunt, magna voce eum vocāvērunt.
(magna vox)
When they saw Quintus, his friends called him in a loud voice.

4 Quīntus eōs summo gaudio salūtāvit.
(summum gaudium)
Quintus greeted them with the utmost joy.

5 magister, clamoribus puerōrum excitātus, ē ianua lūdī exiit puerōsque vultu severo spectāvit.
(clāmōrēs) (iānua) (vultus sevērus)

excitātus roused

Roused by the shouts of the boys, the master went out of the door of the school and looked at the boys with a severe expression.

6 'nōlīte, puerī,' inquit, 'tōtam urbem tantis clamoribus excitāre; intrāte summa celeritate.'
(tantī clāmōrēs) (summa celeritās)
'Boys,' he said, 'don't rouse the whole city with such loud shouts; come in very quickly indeed.'

7 puerī magistro statim pāruērunt. summa diligentia studēbant.
(magister) (summa dīligentia)
The boys obeyed the master at once. They studied with the greatest care.

8 tandem Quīntus magistro dīxit: 'magister, tempus est studiis dēsistere et domum redīre.'
(magister) (studia)

dēsistere to stop (from)

At length Quintus said to the master, 'Master, it's time to stop our studies and return home.'

(d) *Describe in Latin what is happening in this picture:*

____

____

____

____

____

(e) *The following girls' names are all derived from Latin words you know. What did their parents apparently hope their daughters would be like?*

Clara	famous	**Vera**	truthful	**Prudence**	sensible
Gloria	glorious	**Florence**	blooming	**Amanda**	lovable

(f) A swim in the Tiber

In Shakespeare's play *Julius Caesar*, Cassius is trying to persuade Brutus to join him in killing Caesar. He explains how Caesar is not a god but an ordinary man like Brutus and himself:

> I was born free as Caesar; so were you:
> We both have fed as well, and we can both
> Endure the winter's cold as well as he:
> For once, upon a raw and gusty day,
> The troubled Tiber chafing with her shores,
> Caesar said to me 'Darest thou, Cassius, now
> Leap in with me into this angry flood,
> And swim to yonder point?' Upon the word,
> Accoutred as I was, I plunged in
> And bade him follow; so indeed he did.
> The torrent roar'd, and we did buffet it
> With lusty sinews, throwing it aside
> And stemming it with hearts of controversy;
> But ere we could arrive the point proposed,
> Caesar cried 'Help me, Cassius, or I sink!'
> I, as Aeneas, our great ancestor,

Did from the flames of Troy upon his shoulder
The old Anchises bear, so from the waves of Tiber
Did I the tired Caesar. And this man
Is now become a god…

1 How is the character of Caesar presented in this passage? (We see two aspects of it.)

2 How does Cassius's character come across?

3 Explain the reference to Aeneas.

(g) The lines Quintus was writing when Orbilius spotted him (page 149 of your coursebook) are the beginning of a poem he actually wrote in later life. Read them aloud several times and try to feel their rhythm; then translate them:

diffūgēre nivēs, redeunt iam grāmina campīs
arboribusque comae.
mūtat terra vicēs, et dēcrēscentia rīpās
flūmina praetereunt.

diffūgēre = diffūgērunt
comae leaves
mūtat changes
vicēs seasons
dēcrēscentia decreasing, growing smaller (why are the rivers growing smaller?)

(h) Dialogus

Quintus has returned unhappily from school.

Quīntus: salvē, pater.
Flaccus: salvē, cāre fīlī. quid in lūdō hodiē fēcistī?
Quīntus: pater, valdē trīstis sum. Orbilius mē verberāvit.
Flaccus: cūr tē verberāvit Orbilius? num tē male gessistī?
Quīntus: Orbilius poēma Naeviī expōnēbat; ego eum nōn audiēbam quod poēma tam frīgidum erat.
Flaccus: Orbilium nōn audiēbas? quid faciēbās?
Quīntus: ego carmen ipse scrībēbam.
Flaccus: nōn rēctē faciēbās, fīlī. semper dēbēs magistrum audīre.
Quīntus: vēra dīcis, pater. Orbilium mē vīdit scrībentem iussitque tabulam sibi trādere. ubi tabulam vīdit, valdē īrātus erat.
Flaccus: cūr tam īrātus erat Orbilius?
Quīntus: īrātus erat et quod versūs nōn rēctī erant et quod imāginem magistrī in tabulā scrīpseram.
Flaccus: ō Quīnte, valdē petulāns fuistī. Orbilium nōn culpō quod tē verberāvit.
Quīntus: ō pater, diū in illō lūdō mānsī. tempus est domum redīre.
Flaccus: vēra dīcis, fīlī. tempus est lūdō Orbiliī discēdere. iam iuvenis es. iam dēbēs togam virīlem sūmere et rhētoricae studēre.

verberāvit beat
num surely not
tē gessistī you behaved
frīgidum boring
ipse (my)self
scrībentem writing
imāginem a picture
petulāns naughty
rhētoricae rhetoric

CHAPTER XIX

(a) *Write out the accusative, genitive, dative and ablative of the following phrases:*

(i) haec spēs (singular)	(ii) illī diēs (plural)
hanc spem	illos dies
huius spei	illorum dierum
huic spei	illis diebus
hac spe	illis diebus

(b) *Translate the following verb forms:*

1	capiēbamus	we were taking	**7**	fūgerunt	they (have) fled	**13**	fēcī	I did, have done
2	cape	take (sing.)	**8**	fugite	flee! (plur.)	**14**	fac	do! (sing.)
3	capit	he takes	**9**	fugitis	you are fleeing	**15**	fēcit	he did, has done
4	cēpit	he took, has taken	**10**	fugimus	we are fleeing	**16**	facit	he is doing
5	capere	to take	**11**	fūgimus	we (have) fled	**17**	fēcerant	they had done
6	cēperāmus	we had taken	**12**	fugiēbat	he was fleeing	**18**	faciēbātis	you were doing

(c) *Put the following phrases, consisting of noun + adjective, into (i) the genitive, (ii) the dative case:*

		(i)	(ii)
1	haec lēx	huius legis	huic legi
2	ille ōrātor	illius oratoris	illi oratori
3	iter longum	itineris longi	itineri longo
4	poētae clārī	poetarum clarorum	poetis claris
5	vōx magna	vocis magnae	voci magnae

(d) *Describe in Latin what is happening in this picture:*

____

____

____

____

____

(e) *Make up sentences in English to illustrate the meaning of the following words:*

liberate ______________________________

vulnerable ______________________________

prohibit ______________________________

incendiary ______________________________

capital ______________________________

corporeal ______________________________

(f) *What do you mean if you use the following expressions:*

et tū, Brūte? — You are hurt by the disloyalty of a trusted friend.

vēnī, vīdī, vīcī — You've done something speedily and effectively (I came, I saw, I conquered).

festīnā lentē — One can do something faster if one takes one's time.

cavē canem — Beware of the dog.

tempus fugit — Time moves fast and slips away.

ars longa, vīta brevis — Though life is short, artistic achievement lasts.

labor omnia vincit — Hard work is the key to success.

(g)

1 What is meant by the word 'irony'? What is ironical about the fact that Caesar fell dead beneath the statue of Pompey?

2 Why was the Senate meeting at Pompey's Theatre and not at the Senate House? (If you are stuck, you can find the answer on page 145 of your coursebook.)

3 What is the difference between assassination and murder? Do you think that assassination is ever justified? If so, when?

(h) Dialogus

Quintus tells his father about the riot in the forum.

Quīntus: pater, nōn potuī ad scholam Hēliodōrī pervenīre. vix tūtus domum ēvāsī.
Flaccus: quid accidit, fīlī? nārrā mihi omnia.
Quīntus: ubi ad forum advēnī, turbam ingentem vīdī, quae tōtum forum complēbat.
Flaccus: cūr convēnerat tanta turba? quid faciēbant hominēs?
Quīntus: ego gradūs templī ascendī, unde omnia spectāre poteram. magnam pompam vīdī; magistrātūs corpus Caesaris ad rōstra portābant.
Flaccus: dī immortālēs! cūr corpus Caesaris in forum tulerant?
Quīntus: deinde Antōnius rōstra ascendit ōrātiōnemque ad populum habuit. cīvēs ad furōrem excitāvit. omnēs clāmābant et saxa iaciēbant. corpus Caesaris prō rōstrīs cremāvērunt. ego ē forō ēvāsī domumque recurrī.
Flaccus: dī immortālēs! quid nunc futūrum est? cīvēs furunt. ubīque tumultus, ubīque perīcula. in urbe nōn possumus diūtius manēre. ego dēbeō Venusiam redīre, tū Athēnās nāvigāre, ubi philosophiae studēbis.

accidit happened
quae which
complēbat was filling
pompam procession
tulerant had carried
excitāvit roused
cremāvērunt burnt
futūrum going to happen
ubīque everywhere
diūtius any longer
studēbis you will study

CHAPTER XX

(a) *Give the future of the following verbs (singular only). For example:*

parāre parabo, parabis, parabit

1 vocāre vocabo, vocabis, vocabit

2 dormīre dormiam, dormies, dormiet

3 tenēre tenebo, tenebis, tenebit

4 pōnere ponam, pones, ponet

5 facere faciam, facies, faciet

6 lūdere ludam, ludes, ludet

7 accūsāre accusabo, accusabis, accusabit

8 īre ibo, ibis, ibit

(b) *Translate the following verb forms:*

1 timent they are afraid

2 timēbis you will be afraid

3 timuit he was afraid

4 timuerātis you were afraid

5 timueritis you will have been afraid

6 esse to be

7 fuistī you have been

8 erimus we shall be

9 potuī I was able

10 poterit he will be able

11 dīcam I shall say

12 dīcēbam I was saying

13 dīxeram I had said

14 dīc say!

15 dīcēmus we shall say

16 dīcimus we say

17 dīxerimus we shall have said

18 dīcit he says

19 dīxit he (has) said

20 dīcent they will say

21 dormiam I shall sleep

(c) *Put the verbs in brackets into the future (or future perfect) tense and translate:*

1 pater mē iubet Athēnās abīre; mox ad Graeciam navigabo (nāvigō).

Father orders me to go away to Athens; soon I shall sail to Greece.

2 pater mox domum redit (redeō); nam mātrem sorōremque dēbet cūrāre.

Father will soon go back home; for he must look after my mother and sister.

3 ego, cum Athēnās adveniam/advenero, philosophiae studebo .
(adveniō) (studeō)

When I arrive at Athens, I shall study philosophy.

4 si dīligenter studebis/studueris, multa disces et valdē doctus eris .
(studeō) (discō) (sum)

If you work hard, you will learn many things and you will be very learned.

5 Hēliodōrus mox epistolam ad amīcum scribet .
(scrībit)

Heliodorus will soon write a letter to his friend.

6 'cum Athēnās advenies/adveneris, hanc epistolam amīcō meō trāde.'
(advenīs)

When you arrive at Athens, hand over this letter to my friend.

7 ille tē benignē accipiet et iuvabit .
(accipit) (iuvat)

He will receive you with kindness and will help you.

8 ego paterque hodiē ad portum ibimus .
(īmus)

Father and I will go today to the harbour.

9 ibi nāvem quaeremus , quae ad Graeciam navigabit .
(quaerimus) (nāvigat)

quae which

There we shall look for a ship which will sail to Greece.

10 'Quīnte, cum ā Graeciā domum redibis/redieris , et ego et māter et Argus
(redīs)
tē laetī salutabimus .'
(salūtāmus)

'Quintus, when you come back home from Greece, both I and mother and Argus will greet you happily.'

(d) Make a list of people from your country who have been famous in five of the fields mentioned in the second and fourth paragraphs on page 174 of your coursebook (one person for each field).
Which of them would you say has made the greatest contribution to his or her own field?
What do you feel have been your own country's main contributions to the world's civilization?

(e) This tests the grammar you have learnt in the coursebook. It's challenging. Best of luck!

Across

1 Of a boy (5)
4 To the sad people (9)
9 They cross (9)
10 I stayed (5)
11 Hold back (someone)! (6)
12 He believed (8)
14 We were sending (10)
16 Look!
19 Take!*(4)
20 By fear of the man (6,4)
22 We were present (8)
23 Have dinner, you! (4,2)
26 They were (5)
27 You will sleep (9)
28 Those mothers (6,3)
29 I was afraid (5)

Down

1 We were able (9)
2 They were (5)
3 (I killed the) innocent ** man (8)
4 Your thing (4)
5 Among the safe people (5,5)
6 To the timid*** man(6)
7 I taught well (4,5)
8 He will know (5)
13 The waves of the sea (5,5)
15 They had feared (9)
17 You snatched away (9)
18 They will have thrown (8)
21 The happy women (6)
22 To her (2,3)
24 The high thing (5)
25 Of anger (4)

* sūmō, sūmere
** īnsōns, īnsōntis
*** timidus–a–um

(f) Fābula scaenica

Persōnae: Flaccus, Quīntus, nauta prīmus, nauta secundus, magister nāvis.

Flaccus Quīntusque ad portum advēnērunt; nāvem quaerunt quae ad Graeciam nāvigātūra est. ad nautam accēdunt quī per viam ambulat.

Flaccus: dīc mihi, sī vīs, adestne in portū nāvis quae hodiē ad Graeciam nāvigātūra est?
nauta prīmus: paucae nāvēs ad Graeciam ab hōc portū rēctā nāvigant. dēbētis nāvem quaerere quae Puteolōs nāvigātūra est.
Quīntus: nōn Puteolōs īre volō, sed Athēnās.
nauta: nōlī tē vexāre, puer; cotīdiē multae nāvēs Puteolīs Athēnās iter faciunt.
Flaccus: sed ubi nāvem inveniēmus illūc nāvigātūram?

quae which
nāvigātūra about to sail
sī vīs if you will, please
rēctā straight
volō I want

nauta: venīte mēcum, amīcī. ego vōs dūcam ad nāvem quae hodiē illūc iter faciet.
nauta Flaccum Quīntumque ad parvam nāvem dūcit, quae nōn longē abest.
nauta: ecce, haec nāvis hodiē Puteolōs nāvigābit.
Quīntus: quid dīcis? valdē parva est nāvis. nāvis tam parva vix poterit iter tūtum per apertum mare facere.
nauta: nōlī timēre, amīce. nōn longum est iter. Puteolōs tūtus ante sōlis occāsum adveniēs. ecce, nauta ē nāvī festīnat.
Flaccus ad nautam secundum accēdit.
Flaccus: dīc mihi, sī vīs, haec nāvis Puteolōs nāvigātura est?
nauta secundus: nōn errās. ante sōlis occāsum illūc aderimus.
Flaccus: vīsne tū mē ad magistrum dūcere?
nauta: magister occupātus est. nōn licet eum vocāre.
Flaccus: sed necesse est eum vocāre. nam fīlius meus dēbet hodiē Puteolōs nāvigāre.
nauta: nōlī dēspērāre. ecce, magister ipse adest.
magister: *(clāmat)* omnia parāta sunt. in nāvem statim redī, nauta. tempus est nāvem solvere.
Flaccus: magister, redī. vīsne fīlium meum in nāvem accipere?
magister ad pontem redit.
magister: certē eum accipiam, sī mihi viāticum dederis.
Flaccus: grātias tibi agō. quantum est viāticum?
magister: vīgintī dēnāriōs rogō.
Quīntus: (*susurrat*) pater, nimium rogat magister; nōlī eī vīgintī dēnāriōs dare.
Flaccus: nimium rogās, magister. nōn longum est iter. ego quīndecim dēnāriōs dabō.
magister: nōlī nūgās agere. omnēs viātōrēs vīgintī dēnāriōs dant. sed sī tam pauper es, volō quīndecim accipere.
Flaccus: gratiās tibi agō. valdē benignus es.
magister: festīnāte, statim enim nāvem solvam.
Flaccus, ubi argentum magistrō trādidit, ad fīlium sē vertit.
Flaccus: valē, cāre fīlī. cum Athēnās advēneris, epistolam statim nōbīs mitte. dīligenter studē. sine dubiō ōlim vir doctus eris et clārus. sed nōlī parentum immemor esse, quī tē semper amābunt. puer pius es. dī tē servābunt.
Quīntus: parentum numquam immemor erō. semper vōs amābō. cum prīmum Athēnās advēnerō, epistolam vōbīs mittam. et tū, cum domum redieris, salūtem dā mātrī Horātiaeque et Argō cum ōsculō.
Flaccus: nōlī lacrimāre, cāre fīlī; nōn semper aberis; paucīs annīs redieris et tōtam familiam laetus salūtābis. iam ego domum festīnāre dēbeō, tū nāvem cōnscendere. valē, fīlī cārissime.
Flaccus ōsculum Quīntō dat; sē vertit et in oppidum trīstis ambulat. Quīntus nāvem sōlus cōnscendit.

occāsum setting
vīsne will you?
licet it is allowed
ipse himself
solvere to cast off
pontem the gangway
viāticum fare
nimium too much
nūgās agere play the fool
viātōrēs passengers
ōlim some day
immemor forgetful
pius good
ōsculō a kiss

POSSIBLE ANSWERS ON THE CARTOONS

CHAPTER **I**: Horātia culīnam intrat et Scintillam salūtat. Scintilla cēnam parat.

CHAPTER **II**: Quīntus agrum intrat et Flaccum vocat. Flaccus labōrat. puerum nōn audit.

CHAPTER **III**: Quīntus sub arbore dormit; fessus est. Horātia eum quaerit; ānxia est.

CHAPTER **IV**: Quīntus et Horātia sub arbore/in rīpā iacent; fessī sunt. Argus nōn fessus est; in aquā manet et natat.

CHAPTER **V**: puerī in lūdō sedent. magister īrātus est. nam Quīntus sērō venit. Quīntus magistrum salūtat.

CHAPTER **VII**: Aenēās uxōrem et parvum fīlium ex urbe ad collēs dūcit; patrem in umerīs portat.

CHAPTER **VIII**: Trōiānī Polyphēmum vident (dē monte dēscendentem). valdē timent. Aenēās eōs iubet ad nāvēs currere.

CHAPTER **IX**: Ulixes ex antrō Polyphēmī fugit. Polyphēmus exitum antrī observat. sed Ulixes sē cēlat sub ventre ovis ingentis. Polyphēmus eum vidēre nōn potest, quod caecus est. itaque Ulixes ex antrō tūtus exit/ēvādit/fugit.

CHAPTER **XI**: Horātia in agrum currit. Quīntus et Flaccus in ultimā parte agrī labōrant. Horātia eōs vocat et 'venīte celeriter,' inquit; 'ārdet casa.'

CHAPTER **XII**: mīlitēs per viās oppidī contendunt. multī oppidānī eōs spectant. puer parvus eōs salūtat. imperātor legiōnem dūcit equō vectus, etc.

CHAPTER **XIII**: Flaccus Quīntusque Rōmam contendunt. Horātia cum eīs ad prīmum mīliārium venit. Quīntus Horātiam valēre iubet; et Horātia et Argus valdē trīstēs sunt.

CHAPTER **XIV**: Flaccus Quīntusque ad canālem accēdunt. ibi nāvem vident ad rīpam religātam. multī hominēs/viātōrēs nāvem cōnscendunt. nautae mūlam ad nāvem dūcunt.

CHAPTER **XVI**: Quīntus ad lūdum Orbiliī venit. Orbilius puerōs iussit in aulā paulīsper lūdere. cēterī lūdunt sed Quīntus in angulō aulae sōlus stat. nēmō cum eō lūdit.

CHAPTER **XVII**: Cicerō sē vertit et puerōs salūtat. Mārcus Quīntum patrī commendat. Cicerō Quīntum comiter accipit et rogat: 'quid in lūdō hodiē studuistī, Quīnte?'

CHAPTER **XVIII**: Orbilius de poētā frīgidō dīcēbat; Quīntus eum nōn audiēbat sed carmen in tabulā scrībēbat. Orbilius eum vīderat (scribentem) et ad sē vocāverat. Quīntus tabulam eī invītus trādit; ille valdē īrātus est, quod Quīntus nōn modo malum versum scrīpsit sed etiam imāginem/pictūram Orbiliī.

CHAPTER **XIX**: Mārcus Antōnius rōstra ascendit. corpus Caesaris prō rōstrīs iacet. dum Antōnius Caesarem laudat, cīvēs intentē audiunt.

Possible questions for the cartoons.

Teachers can make up their own, once they get the hang of it.

CHAPTER **I**:

(You will have to give the meaning of ‘quis’, ‘quid’ and ‘ubi’.)

1 quis est hic puer?

2 ubi habitat Quīntus? ubi est Apūlia?

3 quis est haec fēmina?

4 quid facit Scintilla?

5 quis est haec puella?

6 ubi est Horātia? quid facit Horātia?

CHAPTER **II**:

1 quis est hic vir?

2 quid facit Flaccus?

3 quis est hic canis?

4 quid facit Argus?

ATTAINMENT TESTS

Attainment test to be taken after CHAPTER VI (40 minutes)

Read the following passage carefully and then answer the questions below:

Scintilla et Horātia ad fontem festīnant. magnās urnās portant.
in viā Quīntum vident; ille lentē ā lūdō redit. mātrem salūtat et 'quid
facitis, mater?' inquit; 'cūr festīnātis?' Scintilla respondet, 'festīnāmus
quod aquam in casā nōn habēmus; et pater iam ab agrō redit.
5 venī hūc et hanc urnam portā.' sed Quīntus 'ad silvam festīnō,' inquit;
'omnēs amīcī mē exspectant.' et in silvam currit.

Scintilla irāta est; 'cūr nōn iuvat nōs Quīntus?' inquit; 'malus puer est.
venī, Horātia; festīnā.' ad fontem adveniunt et aquam celeriter dūcunt.
ad casam lentē redeunt, quod urnae gravēs sunt. Horātia mox fessa est;
10 in terrā sedet, labōre cōnfecta. sed Scintilla Flaccum videt; ille bovēs ab
agrō redūcit. Scintilla eum vocat et 'Flacce,' inquit, 'manē. exspectā nōs.
aquam ā fonte portāmus et valdē fessae sumus.' Flaccus ad eās accurrit
et 'ecce!' inquit, 'adsum. tū, Horātia, urnam trāde et bovēs cūrā.' Horātia
laeta urnam trādit et bovēs dūcit. Scintilla et Flaccus urnās portant et
15 mox omnēs ad casam adsunt.

urnās water pots
quod because
habēmus we have
hanc this
dūcunt they draw
gravēs heavy
labōre cōnfecta worn out by toil
bovēs oxen
trāde hand over
cūrā look after

1 Translate the first paragraph. (30)

2 How does Scintilla feel when Quintus runs off, and why does she feel like this? (1+2)

3 Why do Scintilla and Horatia come back from the spring more slowly than they go there? What does Horatia do when she gets tired? (2+1)

4 At the end of the passage what are (a) Horatia and (b) Flaccus doing? Why is Horatia now **laeta** (l. 14)? (1+1+1)

5 Give one example each of the following from the second paragraph: a verb in the 3rd person singular; a verb in the 1st person plural; a verb in the imperative; an adverb. (4)

6 What case are the following words in and why? Are they singular or plural? **fontem** (l. 8); **urnās** (l. 14); **omnēs** (l. 15) (6)

7 Give an English word derived from **agrō** (l. 11). (1)

TOTAL: 50

Attainment test to be taken after CHAPTER X (40 minutes)

Read the following passage carefully and then answer the questions below:

On his voyage home from Troy, Odysseus (Ulixēs) comes to the island of Circe

Ulixēs, dum ab urbe Trōiā domum nāvigat, ad īnsulam venit
ignōtam. comitēs iubet in lītore manēre, sed ipse collem ascendit.
ubi ad summum collem advenit, fūmum videt in caelum surgentem.
ad nāvem redit et aliōs comitum iubet prope nāvem manēre, aliōs
5 in īnsulam mittit; 'in īnsulam festīnāte,' inquit. 'quis hīc habitat?
cognōscere cupiō.'

illī in īnsulam festīnant et tandem casam in silvā vident. ubi
ad casam accēdunt, multōs lupōs multōsque leōnēs prope casam
vident. valdē timent. mox fēminam audiunt canentem. ubi clāmant,
10 Circē ē iānuā casae exit eōsque in casam vocat. ūnus sōlus extrā
manet, quod perīculum timet; cēterōs Circē in casam dūcit et 'sedēte,'
inquit, 'et cēnāte.'

sed mala venēna cibō miscet. ubi cibum edunt, statim suēs fiunt.
deinde Circē eōs in stabulum suum pellit iubetque in terrā iacēre.

ignōtam unknown
ipse he himself
summum the top of
surgentem rising
aliōs some
quis who
cognōscere to find out
lupōs wolves
leōnēs lions
canentem singing
extrā outside
perīculum danger
mala venēna poisons
cibō in the food
miscet she mixes
edunt they eat
suēs pigs
fiunt they become
stabulum pigsty
pellit she drives

1 Translate the first paragraph. (25)

2 What do Odysseus's companions see when they explore the island? What do they see next? What is their reaction? (1+2+1)

3 What is Circe doing when they come to her house? Why does she come out to see them? (2)

4 One man does not accept Circe's invitation. What does he do and why? (2)

5 What does Circe do to Odysseus's companions? (4)

6 What part of what verbs are the following: **exit** (l. 10); **sedēte** (l. 11), **iacēre** (l. 14)? (3)

7 In what case are the following words, and why: **silvā** (l. 7); **multōs** (l. 8); **casae** (l. 10)? (6)

8 Give one example each from the second paragraph of: a preposition followed by an ablative (not **in**); a preposition followed by an accusative; an adverb; an imperative. (4)

TOTAL: 50

Attainment test to be taken after CHAPTER XV (40 minutes)

Read the following passage carefully and then answer the questions below:

The hero Hercules and the monster Cacus

quondam Flaccus fīlium suum per forum ad collem Palātīnum Tiberimque
flūmen dūcit, et templa parva casāsque flūminī vicīnās Quīntō ostendit.
deinde fābulam fīliō nārrāvit: 'multōs abhinc annōs, antequam
Rōmulus Rōmam condidit, rēx Evander illīc habitābat. in casīs parvīs
5 populus pauper tum vīvēbat sed contentī omnēs erant et laetī; ūnum
sōlum perīculum timēbant.
nam spēlunca erat prope flūmen in colle. illīc habitābat mōnstrum
saevum, sēmihomō, nōmine Cācus. flammās ex ōre spīrābat, hominēs
rapiēbat et crūdēliter interficiēbat. sīc populum omnem diū terrēbat.
10 sed tandem hērōs quīdam advēnit quī eōs illō terrōre līberāvit.
Quīntus 'quis,' inquit, 'tantum labōrem temptāre audēbat? nōnne valdē
audāx fuit?'
respondit Flaccus: 'Herculēs illud opus temptāvit, hērōs clārus. nam ad eum
locum advēnerat cum taurīs ingentibus, quōs ex Hispāniā ad Graeciam dūcēbat.
15 Cācus, ubi taurōs vīdit, cōnstituit eōs rapere. itaque dum Herculēs dormit, in
spēluncam eōs dūxit. postrīdiē, ubi Herculēs exiit, taurōs vidēre nōn potuit.
diū quaerēbat. tandem mūgītum taurōrum audīvit. summā īrā commōtus ad
spēluncam accessit collemque dīripuit; sīc spēluncam ad lūcem aperuit
Cācumque oppugnāvit. Cācus territus erat et vix restitit. sīc facile vincit eum
20 Herculēs, et mōnstrum illud horrendum in terrā iacet mortuum.'

quondam once
vicīnās next to
abhinc ago
antequam before
contentī content
spēlunca cave
mōnstrum monster
ōre mouth
spīrābat breathed
rapiēbat seized
quīdam a certain
quī who
illō terrōre from that fear
līberāvit freed
taurīs bulls
ingentibus huge
quōs which
mūgītum the mooing
dīripuit tore open
illud horrendum that terrible

1 How did Flaccus make sure that he and his son had a good view of the buildings by the Tiber? (2)

2 Describe the living conditions in Rome when Evander was king there. How did the people feel about living there? (2+3)

3 **sēmihomō** (l. 8): 'semi' = half. How do you visualize Cacus? (2)

4 In what two ways is the horrific nature of Cacus conveyed (ll. 8–9)? (2)

5 Translate ll. 11–12. Try to give the correct force to the meaning of the word **nōnne** in l. 11. (3+2)

6 In what case are the following words and why: **forum** (l. 1); **flammās** (l. 8)? (4)

7 What part of what verbs are the following: **condidit** (l. 4); **habitābat** (l. 7)? (4)

8 Give an English word derived from **populus** (l. 5). (1)

9 Translate ll. 13–20. (25)

TOTAL: 50

Attainment test to be taken after CHAPTER XX (1 hour)

Read the following passage carefully and then answer the questions below:

Meanwhile at Venusia...

dum Quīntus cum patre in urbe aberat, māter sororque in oppidō parvō
manēbant; vītam solitam agēbant, rēs domesticās cūrābant, in agrō labōrābant.
sed trīstēs erant et ānxiae. Scintilla semper dē virō timēbat, Horātia patrem
frātremque valdē dēsīderābat; Argus quoque miser erat quod eōs tam diū nōn
5 vīderat. cotīdiē Scintilla vīnum flōrēsque Laribus prō Flaccō offerēbat; saepe
ad templum ībat deōsque ōrābat fīlium virumque cūrāre.
quondam dum in casā sedent, amīcus quīdam incurrit; 'Scintilla,' inquit,
'surge. nūntius ad oppidum Rōmā advēnit; epistolam tibi fert. nōlī dēsperāre.
sine dubiō Flaccus ad vōs mox redībit.' Scintilla surgit et cum Horātiā in viam
10 festīnat nūntiumque quaerit. invēnērunt eum in forō epistolamque accēpērunt.
Scintilla epistolam celeriter legit et 'gaudē, fīlia,' inquit; 'pater iam redit;
Rōmā hodiē discessit paucīsque diēbus domum advēnerit!'
paucīs post diēbus in casā sedēbant cum Flaccus hortum intrāvit. Argus in
aulā iacēbat; iam canis vetus erat quī vix sē movēre poterat. sed ubi Flaccum
15 vīdit, caput tollit et lātrāvit. Flaccus ad eum accessit manūque mulsit; ille
surgere temptāvit. caudam prae gaudiō movet, Flaccī manum lambit; deinde
ad terram cecidit mortuus.
intereā Scintilla Argum audīverat lātrantem; ad iānuam cucurrit Flaccumque
cōnspexit. 'ō Flacce,' inquit, 'rediistīne tandem? oculīs meīs crēdere vix
20 possum.' in bracchia eius ruit et ōscula identidem dedit accēpitque. Horātia
quoque ad patrem cucurrit manumque eius tenēbat. prīmum nec Scintilla nec
Horātia quicquam dīcere potuērunt. tandem tamen Scintilla lacrimās retinuit et
'Quīntus, Flacce,' inquit, 'ubi est? cūr eum relīquistī? quid agit?' Flaccus
respondit, 'Quīntus valet. nōlīte timēre. iam ad Graeciam nāvigat brevīque
25 tempore Athēnās advēnerit.' deinde omnem rem uxōrī fīliaeque nārrāvit.

solitam usual
domesticās domestic
dēsīderābat missed
prō on behalf of
quondam once
fert he is carrying
post later
lātrāvit barked
mulsit stroked
caudam tail
prae gaudiō for joy
lambit licks
lātrantem barking
bracchia arms
ōscula kisses
identidem again and again
quicquam anything

1 Translate 11. 1–12. (30)

2 Flaccus enters the garden where Argus is lying. In what condition is Argus now? How does he greet his master at first? How does he show his delight (l. 16)? What happens to him now? (2+2+3+1)

3 Translate Scintilla's words **oculīs meīs vix crēdere possum** (11. 19–20). With what actions do (a) Scintilla and (b) Horatia greet Flaccus? (3+2+2)

4 What is Scintilla's cause for concern and how does Flaccus reassure her? (2+3)

5 What part of what verbs are the following: **poterat** (1. 14); **cucurrit** (1. 18); **advēnerit** (1. 25)? (6)

6 What case are the following words in and why: **sē** (1. 14); **eius** (1. 20)? (4)

TOTAL: 60

ANSWERS TO THE ATTAINMENT TESTS

Attainment test to be taken after CHAPTER VI.

1 Scintilla and Horatia hurry to the spring. They carry large water pots. On the road they see Quintus; he is coming back slowly from school. He greets his mother and says, 'What are you doing, mother? Why are you hurrying?' Scintilla replies, 'We are hurrying because we do not have water in the house; and father is now coming back from the field. Come here and carry this water pot.' But Quintus says, 'I'm hurrying to the wood; all my friends are waiting for me.' And he runs into the wood. (30)

2 She feels angry (1) because Quintus has been a bad boy in not helping them (2).

3 The water pots are now heavy because they are full of water (2). She sits on the ground (1).

4 (a) Horatia is leading the oxen (1) and (b) Flaccus is carrying the water pots (1). Horatia is happy because she has got rid of her (heavy) water pot (1).

5 **est/iuvat/inquit/sedet/videt/reducit/vocat/accurrit/tradit/ducit** (1); **portamus/sumus** (1); **veni/festina/mane/exspecta/trade/cura** (1); **lente/celeriter/mox/valde** (1).

6 accusative, after **ad**, singular (2); accusative, object of verb, plural (2); nominative, subject of verb, plural (2).

7 agriculture/agricultural (1).

Attainment test to be taken after CHAPTER X.

1 While Ulysses sails home from the city of Troy, he comes to an unknown island. He orders his companions to stay on the shore, but he climbs a hill. When he reaches the top of the hill, he sees smoke rising into the sky. He goes back to the ship and orders some of his companions to stay near the ship and sends some into the island. 'Hurry into the island,' he says. 'Who lives here? I want to know.' (25)

2 a house (1); many wolves and (many) lions (2); they are very afraid (1).

3 singing (1); they shout (1).

4 He stays outside (1) because he is frightened (of the danger) (1).

5 She gives them food mixed with poison (1); they become pigs (1); she drives them into her pigsty (1) and orders them to lie on the ground (1).

6 third person singular of **exeo** (1); plural imperative of **sedeo** (1); present infinitive of **iaceo** (1).

7 ablative, after **in** (2); accusative, adjective agreeing with **lupos** (or **leones**) (2); genitive, of the house (2).

8 **e** (l. 10) (1); **in** (ll. 7, 10, 11)/**ad** (l. 8)/**prope** (l. 8) (1); **tandem** (l. 7)/**valde** (l. 9)/**mox** (l. 9) (1); **sedete** (l. 11)/**cenate** (l. 12) (1).

Attainment test to be taken after CHAPTER XV .

1 He took him up the Palatine Hill (2).

2 They were poor and they lived in small houses (2). They were content and happy (2), but frightened of one thing (1).

3 a subjective answer: brutal, huge, monstrous, animalistic — these are possibilities, but other suggestions may well qualify for marks (2).

4 He breathed flames (from his mouth) (1) and (snatched and) killed men (1).

5 Quintus said, 'Who dared to attempt so great a task? (3) He must have have been very bold, mustn't he?' (or similar) (2).

6 accusative, after **per** (2); accusative, object of verb (2).

7 3rd person singular of the perfect of **condo** (2); 3rd person singular of the imperfect of **habito** (2).

8 population/populate/populace (1).

9 Flaccus answered, 'Hercules, a famous hero, attempted that task. For he had come to this place with some huge bulls which he was leading from Spain (Hispania) to Greece. When Cacus saw the bulls, he decided to seize them. And so, while Hercules was asleep, he led them into his cave. The next day, when Hercules came out, he could not see the bulls. He searched for a long time. At length he heard the mooing of the bulls. Moved with the utmost anger, he went to the cave and tore open the hill; thus he opened the cave to the light and attacked Cacus. Cacus was terrified and scarcely resisted. Thus Hercules easily overcame/overcomes him, and that terrible monster lay/lies on the ground dead.' (25)

Attainment test to be taken after CHAPTER XX.

1 While Quintus was away with his father in the city, his mother and sister stayed in the little town; they led their usual life, they looked after their domestic affairs, (and) they worked in the field. But they were sad and anxious. Scintilla was always afraid about her husband, (while) Horatia very much missed her father and brother; Argus also was miserable because he had not seen them

for so long. Every day Scintilla offered wine and flowers to the household gods on behalf of Flaccus; she often went to the temple and begged the gods to look after her son and husband.

Once while they were sitting in the house, a certain friend ran in; 'Scintilla,' he said, 'get up. A messenger has come to the town from Rome; he's bringing you a letter. Do not despair. Without doubt Flaccus will soon come back to you.' Scintilla got/gets up and hurried/hurries with Horatia into the road and looked/looks for the messenger. They found him in the forum and took the letter. Scintilla quickly read/reads the letter and said, 'Rejoice, daughter; your father is already on his way back; he left Rome today and in a few days will have arrived home!' (30)

2 He is old and can scarcely move (2); he lifts his head and barks (2); he tries to get up, he moves his tail for joy, he licks Flaccus's hand (3); he falls to the ground dead (1).

3 I can scarcely believe my eyes. (3) (a) Scintilla rushes into Flaccus's arms and they exchange many kisses (2); (b) Horatia runs to her father and holds his hand (2).

4 She is worried about Quintus (2); Quintus is well (1); he's sailing to Greece (1) and will soon be in Athens (1).

5 3rd person singular of the imperfect of **possum** (2); 3rd person singular of the perfect of **curro** (2); 3rd person singular of the future perfect of **advenio** (2).

6 accusative, object of verb/part of reflexive verb (2); genitive, of him, his (2).

NOTES ON THE ILLUSTRATIONS

p. 9 Our photograph shows the Roman theatre at Hierapolis (now Pamukkale in Turkey). Extraordinarily well-preserved, it was built around the start of the third century AD. Its travertine seats hold 15,000 spectators. The stage has been restored.

p. 17 The Laocoon group dates from the first century AD and is ascribed to the Rhodian sculptors Agesander, Polydoros and Athenodoros. It was found on the Esquiline Hill in Rome in 1506. The dreadful pain on Laocoon's face, the agonized tension of his muscles and the pitiful contortions of the bodies are key factors in the violent realism of the sculptors' conception. The group stands in the Vatican and Lord Byron (*Childe Harold's Pilgrimage*, Canto IV, CLX) recommends a visit there:

Or, turning to the Vatican, go see
Laocoon's torture dignifying pain —
A father's love and mortal's agony
With an immortal's patience blending: Vain
The struggle; vain, against the coiling strain
And gripe, and deepening of the dragon's grasp,
The old man's clench; the long envemon'd chain
Rivets the living links, — the enormous asp
Enforces pang on pang, and stifles gasp on gasp.

p. 21 From left to right:

1 The head of Odysseus from the group discribed below. It is original, not a reproduction.
2 The blinding of the Cyclops by Odysseus and his men. Largely a reconstruction, it stands in the Museum at Sperlonga, Italy. This group, probably by the sculptors of the Laocoon group (see note above) dates from the first century AD and was found in the so-called Grotto of Tiberius where the emperor may have had a narrow escape from falling rocks. The cave was excavated in 1957–60.
3 A head of the Cyclops from the first century BC in the Museum of Fine Arts, Boston.

p. 34 Our photograph is from Trajan's column. This column was dedicated in 113 AD to commemorate the emperor's conquest of the Dacians (the inhabitants of modern Rumania). Carved with a continuous spiral relief illustrating the Dacian campaigns, it is an unrivalled source of information about Roman warfare. Our illustration shows Roman soldiers setting off from camp. On tent poles over their left shoulders they are carrying a heavy load of kit, including a pack, a bottle for wine and cooking pots.

p. 38 The Appian Way near Rome. This, the first of the great Roman roads, was planned by the blind Appius Claudius in 312 BC. It is still used by traffic, though quite close to the section illustrated it is now rudely bisected by the modern peripheral road round the city.

p. 51 This statue of a young man wearing a toga and holding a scroll, which he has presumably taken from the box by his feet, dates from the first century BC. It stands in the Belvedere courtyard of the Vatican in Rome, not far from the Lacoon group.